*The Evidence of God
in an Expanding Universe*

The Evidence of God
in an Expanding Universe

FORTY AMERICAN SCIENTISTS
DECLARE THEIR AFFIRMATIVE
VIEWS ON RELIGION

*Published in Connection
with the International Geophysical Year*

EDITED BY *John Clover Monsma*

G. P. PUTNAM'S SONS   NEW YORK

CONTENTS

[4

5]

[6

EDITOR'S INTRODUCTION

ONLY a month or two before this book went to press a Texas biology professor told the American Association for the Advancement of Science, meeting in Indianapolis, that man is not really an animal but a plant. Man, he pontificated, is the result of developments in the internal structure of living plant cells, and yellow algae (microscopic water plants) and red and brown seaweed are part of his ancestry. How to account for this evolutionary process? The process is unknown, admitted the professor. He seemed never to have heard of God or creation.

Just previous to this incident a college graduate was denied admission to the University of Miami school of education because of his "militant and fanatical" views on atheism. It was explained that the education course he desired includes interning as an instructor in the public schools, and that the county school board refused to put its children in the hands of an atheist. The "Free Thinkers of America" hired a lawyer to bring pressure to bear upon the board, and the case is still pending.

Almost at the same time a Student Council committee at Harvard, after polling and tabulating undergraduate opinion, brought in a report on the students' religious beliefs and attitudes. Of the 190 students polled 40 refused to commit themselves. Of the remainder 40 percent were church attendants, and 79 percent considered questions about the existence of God of "considerable" or "very great" importance. The committee urged more religion courses for undergraduates and asked in all seriousness, "What is the meaning of existence? Is there a God?" and asserted, "These questions are weighty and cosmic. . . ."

Just a few snapshots, these, of present-day American educational life. A widely read national magazine described the questions and remarks of the Harvard committee, just quoted, as "a bit of undergraduate pomposity." There, in my view, is a snapshot of a section of American *public*, or at least journalistic, life!

"Is there a God?" Months before the Harvard young men inserted this question in their report I had sent it to a large number of American men of science, inviting them to answer it candidly and to grant me permission to have their answers published in a book. Forty of the answers are herewith presented to the reading public. They naturally vary greatly in approach, thought and style—and each writer is responsible for his own production. I was merely the editor. But let me say this: all the chapters, all forty of them, are one in spirit, one in goal, one in fundamental convictions. The genuine enthusiasm of our scientist-writers for the idea of this book was most heartening. I am deeply grateful to all our collaborators.

*   *   *

As to the need of this book, I must state that the "snapshots" presented can be greatly multiplied, both in our own country and abroad. One can hardly blame the vast number of parents these days who hesitate to send their children to many of the high schools and colleges, fearing that they will turn religious skeptics. Parents are in error, of course, when they blame science and scientific instruction *as such* for these dangers. The contents of this book should help them see the light, in this respect.

It is hoped that both students and their instructors—the tens of thousands of them, all through the world—may be benefited by what our scientist-writers have produced. "At sea," "on the fence," "betwixt and between," are colloquialisms that aptly describe the mental attitude of many in scholastic circles with reference to the existence of God and His relation to the universe. I am afraid the same holds true of a rather large section of the more intelligent general public. May this book help point the course.

This seems to be an opportune and most fitting time to put a volume of this type at the public's disposal, seeing we are in the midst of the International Geophysical Year, in which more than sixty nations are participating. Thousands of scientists, the world over, are delving and reaching into the "mysteries" of the universe, and a clarion-like testimony concerning the God of the universe, not by theologians this time, but by professional scientists, seems truly desirable.

As the book was nearing the print shop "sputnik" came on the world scene and public interest in scientific accomplishments and exploratory endeavors rose to unwonted heights. Men's minds suddenly broke out of the encystment of little everyday earth affairs and soared wonderingly to astral altitudes. As a scientific event we naturally welcomed "sputnik." We shared in the general, tremulous excitement. But at the same time our thoughts were directed, and most forcefully, to the land of "sputnik's" origin.

It is generally known that a considerable part of today's world is being dominated by leaders whose philosophy is that of atheistic materialism. One of the practical results of that philosophy, and of the motivations and inner drives it creates, is extensive technical achievements. Another is ways and means that are, only too frequently, abysmal in horror. When God is "shelved," Divine law, conscience, ethical principles and practical morality will also be shelved, and a barbarism which at the same time is more refined and more brutal than that of the most benighted savages is bound to rear its Apollyon-like head. Our writers have, each of them, a sharp, sturdy arrow, and the whole quiverful of them is directed at that philosophy.

❖   ❖   ❖

The basic postulate of this book, its point of departure, is that science can establish, by the observed facts of Nature and intellectual argumentation, that a super-human Power exists. It cannot identify that Power or describe it, except in very general terms. For identification and more detailed description special revelation (the Bible) is needed. But by proceeding from the basic postulate I feel our scientists have struck effectively at the heart of atheism.

Atheism in Christianized lands is a throwback to paganism. It has been mistakenly argued that monotheism (belief in one God) has slowly and erratically developed from the lowest gradations of paganism. The opposite is the truth: original monotheism has degenerated into the various forms of paganism. Originally man had a *natural sense* of the one eternal God, his own Creator and the Creator of the entire universe. Then this natural sense became adulterated, corrupted. Historically this corruption has expressed itself in (1) animism, (2) fetishism, (3) Nature worship, (4) idolatry —worship of manufactured idols, (5) worship of man—some powerful individual, (6) deification of the State, (7) the dead-end result: atheism.

Many of our modern physico-philosophers have been very great thinkers, but their philosophy was essentially pagan. The same is true of the better known modern biologists, such as Lamarck, Wallace, and Darwin. It may not be widely known, but the great and idolized Darwin himself seems to have grown somewhat skeptical about his thought structure toward the end of his life and stated outright that if even the slightest fault was ever detected in his theory of mechanistic-materialistic evolution the whole structure would, and should, collapse. Such faults actually were detected, but the collapse did not happen. Instead, the Neo-Darwinists arose!

Some of the greatest of modern "pagan" thinkers, devoted followers of Darwin and associates, were honest enough to "backtrack." Reinke of Germany, in his *Die Welt als That,* confessed that there is an "Eternal Intelligence" and an "Eternal Power." Romanes of England, shortly before his death, admitted that his whole scientific and philosophic set-up had been basically wrong, and that the universe cannot possibly be explained without a God. There were other repentants besides these.

13]

A case by itself was that of Michael Faraday, world-renowned English chemist and physicist, who had been theorizing and speculating and building thought structures all his life. One day, in 1867, he lay on his deathbed, and a friend and colleague asked the great scientist, "Faraday, what are your speculations *now*?" "Speculations?" repeated the dying man. "Speculations? I have none! Thank God, I am not resting my dying head upon *speculations*. I *know* whom I have believed and am persuaded that He is able to keep that which I have committed unto Him against that day."

*   *   *

Ever since the day of the great physicists and biologists of the former century, atheistic materialists in western lands have been arguing and contending with one another about the origin and nature of things. This has been true especially of what one might call the minor-calibre scientists. Real top-rank scientists, men of genius in their line, of genuine creative ability, have more and more soft-pedaled the genetical aspect of their theory, or theories. And with the giant-steps forward that science has taken in the past quarter of a century they find themselves almost reduced to silence in things metaphysical.

The reason is clear. Creative scientists have made tremendous strides up the mountain of knowledge, and they have come to see far more than their predecessors did. But the things they saw were not only facts but also problems—problems without number and apparently insoluble. In fact, their ever-widening horizons became dense, fog-beclouded with mysteries. And it stopped them in their ascending tracks. And it made them concentrate on the multitude of freshly discovered facts at their disposal. The result was the numerous technical "wonders" of this present day.

Many of our scientists—as this book will reveal—have become very humble in the process. Others have been humble from the outset. As they learn, ever more, their heads are bowing down, ever more, in adoration.

Some of them, perhaps many of them, have a strange sort of joy in their hearts, a joy "unspeakable and full of glory." For over the fields of *facts*, and through the mist and murk and ever-deepening gloom of *problems*, they have seen, intermittently but assuredly, like an extra-gallactic visitant— the effulgence of the LIGHT.

JOHN CLOVER MONSMA

*The Evidence of God
in an Expanding Universe*

THE ORIGIN OF THE WORLD
—BY CHANCE OR DESIGN?

BY FRANK ALLEN

BIOPHYSICIST

M.A. and Ph.D., Cornell University; Professor of biophysics, University of Manitoba, Canada, 1904–1944; specialist in color vision, physiological optics, liquid air production, glandular mutations. Recipient of Tory Gold Medal, Royal Society of Canada.

IT has often been made to appear that the material universe has not needed a Creator. It is undeniable, however, that the universe exists. Four solutions of its origin may be proposed: first, that it is an illusion—contrary to the preceding statement; second, that it spontaneously arose out of nothing; third, that it had no origin but has existed eternally; fourth, that it was created.

The first proposed solution asserts that there is no problem to solve except the metaphysical one of human consciousness, which has occasionally itself been considered an illusion! The hypothesis of illusion has been lately revived in physical science by Sir James Jeans * who states that from the concepts of modern physics "the universe cannot admit of material representation, and the reason, I think, is that it has become a mere mental concept." Accordingly, one may say that illusory trains apparently filled with imaginary passengers cross unreal rivers on immaterial bridges formed of mental concepts!

The second concept, that the world of matter and energy arose of itself out of nothing, is likewise too absurd a supposition for any consideration.

The third concept, that the universe existed eternally, has one element in common with the concept of creation: either inanimate matter with its incorporated energy, or a Personal Creator, is eternal. No greater intellectual difficulty exists in the one concept than in the other. But the laws of thermodynamics (heat) indicate that the universe is running down to a condition when all bodies will be at the same extremely low temperature and no energy will be available. Life would then be impossible. In infinite time this state of entropy would already have happened. The hot sun and stars, the earth with its wealth of life, are complete evidence that the origin of the universe has occurred in *time,* at a fixed point of time, and therefore the universe must have been *created.* A great First Cause, an eternal, all-knowing and all-powerful Creator must exist, and the universe is His handiwork.

The adjustments of the earth for life are far too numerous to be accounted for by chance. First, the earth is a sphere freely poised in space ("He hangeth the earth upon nothing" —Job 26: 7), in daily rotation on its polar axis, giving the

* *The Mysterious Universe,* p. 169.

alternation of day and night, and in yearly revolution around the sun. These motions give stability to its orientation in space, and, coupled with the inclination (23 degrees) of the polar axis to the plane of its revolution (the ecliptic), affords regularity to the seasons, thus doubling the habitable area of the earth and providing a greater diversity of plant life than a stationary globe could sustain.

Secondly, the atmosphere of life-supporting gases is sufficiently high (about 500 miles) and dense to blanket the earth against the deadly impact of twenty million meteors that daily enter it at speeds of about thirty miles per second. Among many other functions the atmosphere also maintains the temperature within safe limits for life; and carries the vital supply of fresh water-vapor far inland from the oceans to irrigate the earth, without which it would become a lifeless desert. Thus the oceans, with the atmosphere, are the balance-wheel of Nature.

Four remarkable properties of water, its power of absorbing vast quantities of oxygen at low temperatures, its maximum density at 4 degrees C. above freezing whereby lakes and rivers remain liquid, the lesser density of ice than water so that it remains on the surface, and the power of releasing great quantities of heat as it freezes, preserve life in oceans, lakes and rivers throughout the long winters.

The dry land is a stable platform for much terrestrial life. The soil provides the minerals which plant life assimilates and transforms into needful foods for animals. The presence of metals near the surface renders the arts of civilization possible. Surely Isaiah is right (45: 18 R.S.V.) in saying of God: "He did not make it a chaos; He formed it to be inhabited."

The diminutive size of the earth compared with the immensity of space is sometimes disparagingly referred to. If the earth were as small as the moon, if one-fourth its present diameter, the force of gravity (one-sixth that of the earth) would fail to hold both atmosphere and water, and temperatures would be fatally extreme. If double its present diameter, the enlarged earth would have four times its present surface and twice its force of gravity, the atmosphere would be dangerously reduced in height, and its pressure would be increased from 15 to 30 pounds per square inch, with serious repercussions upon life. The winter areas would be greatly increased and the regions of habitability would be seriously diminished. Communities of people would be isolated, travel and communication rendered difficult or almost impossible.

If our earth were of the size of the sun, but retaining its density, gravity would be 150 times as great, the atmosphere diminished to about four miles in height, evaporation of water rendered impossible, and pressures increased to over a ton per square inch. A one-pound animal would weigh 150 pounds, and human beings reduced in size to that of, say, a squirrel. Intellectual life would be impossible to such creatures.

If the earth were removed to double its present distance from the sun, the heat received would be reduced to one-fourth its present amount, the orbital velocity would be only one-half, the winter season would be doubled in length and life would be frozen out. If its solar distance were halved, the heat received would be four times as great, the orbital velocity would be doubled, seasons would be halved in length, if changes could even be effected, and the planet would be too parched to sustain life. In size and distance from the sun, and in orbital velocity, the earth is able to sustain life, so that mankind can enjoy physical, intellectual and spiritual life as it now prevails.

If in the origin of life there was no design, then living matter must have arisen by chance. Now chance, or probability as it is termed, is a highly developed mathematical theory which applies to that vast range of objects of knowledge that are beyond absolute certainty. This theory puts us in possession of the soundest principles on which to discriminate truth from error, and to calculate the likelihood of the occurrence of any particular form of an event.

Proteins are the essential constituents of all living cells, and they consist of the five elements, carbon, hydrogen, nitrogen, oxygen and sulphur, with possibly 40,000 atoms in the ponderous molecule. As there are 92 chemical elements in Nature, all distributed at random, the chance that these five elements may come together to form the molecule, the quantity of matter that must be continually shaken up, and the length of time necessary to finish the task, can all be calculated. A Swiss mathematician,* Charles Eugene Guye, has made the computation and finds that the odds against such an occurrence are 10^{160} to 1, or only one chance in 10^{160}, that is 10 multiplied by itself 160 times, a number far too large to be expressed in words. The amount of matter to be shaken together to produce a single molecule of protein would be millions of times greater than that in the whole universe. For it to occur on the earth alone would require many, almost endless billions (10^{243}) of years.

* Quoted by V. H. Mottram in the organ of the British Broadcasting Corporation, *Listener*, Apr. 22, 1948.

Proteins are made from long chains called amino acids. The way those are put together matters enormously. If in the wrong way they will not sustain life and may be poisons. Professor J. B. Leathes (England) has calculated that the links in the chain of quite a simple protein could be put together in millions of ways (10^{48}). It is impossible for all these chances to have coincided to build one molecule of protein.

But proteins as chemicals are without life. It is only when the mysterious life comes into them that they live. Only Infinite Mind, that is God, could have foreseen that such a molecule could be the abode of life, could have constructed it, and made it live.

A CONCLUSIVE TEST

BY ROBERT MORRIS PAGE

PHYSICIST

B.Sc., Hamline University, M.Sc., George Washington University, Hon. D.Sc., Hamline University. With Naval Research Laboratory, Washington, D.C., since 1927. In 1934 completed first pulse radar in the world for detection of aircraft; received U.S. Navy Distinguished Civilian Service Award, Presidential Certificate of Merit, IRE Fellowship, Harry Diamond Memorial Award, Stuart Ballantyne Medal of the Franklin Institute. Holder of 37 patents, mostly in radar. Author of numerous technical articles and lectures. Presently Associate Director of Research for Electronics, U.S. Naval Research Laboratory. Specialist in precision instrumentation in electronics, administration of research.

THE test of an hypothesis involves the establishment of conditions consistent with the hypothesis to produce results predicted by the hypothesis on the assumption that the hypothesis is true. Thus there are at least three elements necessary to the test of an hypothesis: (1) meeting specified conditions, (2) to produce predicted results, (3) on the assumption of validity of the hypothesis. The first two conditions are generally accepted without argument; the third

25]

is a more subtle point that frequently escapes recognition as a necessary element in the test of any hypothesis.

When ships were built of wood because it was commonly believed that in order to float they had to be built of materials lighter than water, the proposition was made that ships could be built of iron and still float. A certain blacksmith stated that ships built of iron could not float because iron would not float, and he proved his point by tossing a horseshoe into a tub of water. His assumption that the hypothesis was untrue foreclosed the possibility of his devising an experiment consistent with the hypothesis which might have produced the result predicted by the hypothesis. Had he assumed the hypothesis to be true, he would have tossed an iron wash basin into the tub of water instead of an iron horseshoe.

Sometimes a full test of an hypothesis requires observations that are not available to a particular observer. For example, suppose an observer is limited in his observation to the surface of the ocean. This observer can see nothing that is above or below the surface of the water and is aware of the presence of objects only through a breaking of the water surface by contact. This observer can be aware of any object floating on the water. Thus all boats, however large or small, or floating debris and birds swimming on the surface may be available for observation. Birds or airplanes flying through the air, fish or submarines below the surface, are non-existent as far as the observer is concerned. A submerged object coming to the surface, or a bird alighting on the water appear to the observer as a creating of something out of nothing. The inverse process appears as annihilation. To this observer a large body of phenomena will be familiar and more or less well understood, namely phenomena associated with objects floating on the water. However, certain phenomena appearing occasionally and unpredictably could not be explained; such, for example, as the sudden appearance or disappearance of a bird alighting on the water or taking off from the water.

Let us assume that this observer meets an informer who can see birds and airplanes flying through the air and who can peer beneath the surface and see fishes and submarines. If there is communication between the two, many phenomena previously observed but unexplained can now be explained and understood. However, the existence of so radical a concept as sub-surface swimming or super-surface flying would be very difficult for our original observer to accept. He would tend to disbelieve his informer until the informer's own veracity could in some way be checked. This might be rather difficult to do. However, one thing that the informer could do to establish his authenticity with the observer would be to predict, through his observations of things which only he could see, occurrences which our observer could later observe but could not explain. For example, the informer may observe a bird about to dive into the water to capture a fish also observed by the informer. He may then tell our observer that he is about to see a sudden separation in the surface of the water as a bird passed through the surface. This separation would be followed by the emergence of the bird, carrying a fish back into the air. When this prediction is fulfilled our observer will have at least some evidence that his informer knows what he is talking about and is telling the truth.

With this brief introduction, let us now turn to the idea

of the existence of God and categorize that idea, as it is categorized in some minds, as an hypothesis. As we turn our attention to the problem of testing that hypothesis, these are the things we find:

First, for the purpose of making a valid test we must assume, for the time being at least, that the hypothesis is true. Whether or not we believe it, we must make the assumption for the purpose of the test. Otherwise, we will be incapable of making a valid test.

Second, we must be prepared to accept the testimony of many that our powers of observation are limited to a relatively small portion of all reality. The hypothesis that there is a God includes certain conditions relative to the existence of God which are beyond the province of science to test. The testimony of many is that God is a spirit, and, as such, exists in a realm of reality which is not wholly included in the physical universe, not restricted within three spatial dimensions, and not subject to the laws of time as we know them. We must be prepared to recognize that our physical universe, all contained within certain dimensions of space and time, may be only a small part of all reality, just as the surface of the sea is only a small part of all space known to us.

Third, assuming that there is a God, we must be prepared to deal seriously with the concept that that God is capable of revealing to us information concerning reality beyond our physical universe.

Tests as described above have been made by many investigators, including the author. The author has found in the Christian Bible a very large amount of information concerning the spiritual world. This information has come into the Bible through human agencies, that is, through men who wrote what they believed and what they knew to be true. The authenticity of the writings of these men, though the men themselves are human, is established by such things as the prediction of highly significant events far in the future that could be accomplished only through knowledge obtained from a realm which is not subject to the laws of time, as we know them. The prediction of future events is not the only evidence, but is given as an example of one type of evidence, which is used to establish the authenticity of the testimony of our informers, the men who wrote the Bible.

One of the great evidences is the long series of prophecies concerning Jesus, the Messiah. These prophecies extend for hundreds of years prior to the birth of Christ. They include a vast amount of detail concerning Christ himself, His nature, and things which He would do when He came—things which to the natural world, or to the scientific world, remain to this day completely inexplicable. The historical appearance of the Christ as prophesied, with the fulfillment of all the many things that were prophesied, a fulfillment that is so firmly established historically as to be doubted only by those with little knowledge, has authenticated not only the prophecies concerning Him but also the validity of His teachings when He came.

The clinching argument for the validity of our fundamental hypothesis is a personal and private matter, one which arises only in the personal experience of individuals.

When one participates in experiments in which all of the implications of the hypothesis as derived from our informers are taken into account, one can observe whether or not the predicted results are actually obtained.

When one studies the relationships which can and should exist between man and God, when one studies the conditions that man must fulfill to establish these relationships, and when one seriously and wholeheartedly sets about to fulfill those conditions, the achievement of the predicted relationships results with such overwhelming influence in the person's life that there can be no room for doubt in the person's mind. God becomes an intimate personal reality of such nearness and such magnitude that faith grows to the proportions of positive knowledge.

THE LESSON OF THE ROSEBUSH

BY MERRITT STANLEY CONGDON

NATURAL SCIENTIST AND PHILOSOPHER

Ph.D., Sc.D., Webster University, S.T.D., Burton University; formerly Professor of Basic Science, Trinity College, Florida; member of American Physical Society, Mediaeval Academy of America, and numerous other scientific groups. Specialist in psychology, physics, philosophy of science, Biblical research.

MANY years ago I saw a beautiful, cultivated rosebush in bloom beside a lonely road in Pennsylvania. When I passed the place later, I noticed near the bush the crumbling remains of a cellar wall covered with weeds and briars. There was no building for at least half a mile. Assuming the utter improbability that this rosebush had resulted by chance from some seed or viable fragment of a far-distant bush carried by wind, water, fowl or mammal, I *knew* intuitively that some mature human being had carefully planted it near his home. I did not see it planted nor did I have any historical source to consult, but I was forced to the irresistible conclusion that it could have come to its

31]

present location and condition only by human agency and intervention.

At first we might decry the use of this kind of analogical inference in the fields of science, but we are promptly confronted with the fact that this is indeed the very type of evidence upon which our oldest natural science, astronomy, is founded. We cannot coerce the galaxies, stars or planets from their orbits for experimental investigation. We cannot eliminate cosmic rays from the scene. The Doppler Effect (change in number of sound and light waves, depending on distance) may perhaps be radically influenced by gigantic distances, and the continuous acceleration of the speed of remotely distant nebulae may possibly outrun that of light beyond the "cosmic curtain," shutting off any further view of them. But we cannot alter or modify these factors. We can observe them at a distance, but we cannot experiment with them.

Therefore, we must depend upon the *probability* involved in analogous processes among the galaxies, just as we depend upon the laws governing mass and energy even among the elementary particles of the atoms. Although we can distinctly see the stars and nebulae and can discern the nature of their apparent and real movements, so far we have never seen directly any component of the atom. And yet, that first atomic bomb thoroughly supported and vindicated our theoretical interpretations of the structure and functions of the invisible atom. Both of these groups of entities (galaxies and atoms) can indeed be defined operationally, and can also be sustained by logical inference from empirical (experimental) data.

Of course, the cosmic object (totality of external phenomena) must have powers and traits which are truly analogous to our own. This means that some consistent pattern for what we call "personality" must be provided in the cosmic framework. Such a provision would necessarily require the assistance of metaphysics (the non-physical or supernatural) in establishing a rational ground for any dualistic concept, for behavioristic psychology by itself seems to be unable to provide that ground.

I have often demanded of my students that they tell me the exact chemical formula for a "thought," the exact length in centimeters, the exact weight in grams, its color, its form or shape, its potential pressures or inner tensions, its "field," and its location or its direction and speed of movement. They could not describe a thought in *any* physical terms, equations or formulas. A new vocabulary had to be introduced which lacked the accepted designations or "signs" and the conventional meanings of the vocabulary of physical science.

This problem cannot be merely "laughed off," for if the cosmos be not dyadic (consisting of two parts or elements), *then the problem of human "thought" has never been dealt with seriously.* And if a monistic (unitary; consisting of one element) contention insists upon a purely material essence in thought, then we must demand its *complete* description in physical terms alone. *This has never been done.* The materialistic postulates of Democritus, Hobbes or the modern behaviorists, or the idealistic presuppositions of Leibnitz, Berkeley or Hegel, are merely speculative hypotheses without even empirical foundation as far as experimental validation is concerned. The validity of any philosophy of Nature can be and should be challenged, unless such a philosophy furnishes an adequate rationale which deals with *all* types of facts, factors, features and elements in the natural universe.

Science is tested knowledge, but it is still subject to human vagaries, illusions and inaccuracies. It is legitimate only within the confines of its own areas. It is rigidly restricted to quantitative data for description and prediction. It begins and ends with probability, not certainty. Its results are approximations subject to "probable error," especially in measurements and correlations. Its products are tentative and are modified frequently by new data. There is no *finality* in scientific inferences. The scientist says: "Up to the present, the facts are thus and so."

Science starts from undeniable axioms and precepts which are not essentially dependent upon physical reality. Thus science erects its systematized knowledge upon philosophical foundations. Personal experience, in science as in philosophy and religion, is the ultimate test of all truth, and becomes the final arbiter. Any inference made by one scientist must prove to be true and valid for all scientists. Yet, our individual perceptions of natural phenomena are highly conditioned and relative.

Nevertheless, these limitations do not destroy the positive values and virtues of the scientific approach, but they do channel the efforts and circumscribe the results. Consequently, natural science is utterly unable to deal directly with problems which are largely devoid of entities susceptible of quantitative analysis and synthesis. The question "Is there a personal God?" is *prima facie* such a problem. But if there are definite impingements of the spiritual entities upon the material entities, this fact becomes an appropriate concern of natural science. And any legitimate manner or method of dealing with it effectively must be accepted, including analogical inference.

There are many indications that the processes of Nature and of science, although they cannot fully confirm or refute the existence or functioning of non-material entities, do not preclude the *probability* of realities in realms beyond the purely physical. By analogy to our own intelligent agency in a world fraught with rational values, we must accept the implications of similar rational activity and intelligent control involved in the bell-shaped curve of distribution (even in the electron orbits), the "water cycle," the "carbon dioxide cycle," the amazing processes of biological reproduction, the vital process of photosynthesis for storing solar energy for the living things of earth—*ad infinitum.* How, indeed, can we conceive of any arbitrary or fortuitous initiation of such processes without intelligent agency? How do the abstractions concerning uniformity and universality, causality and integration, teleology and interfunction, or conservation and equilibrium continue age after age to satisfy the demands of an activated cosmos? How could they operate rationally throughout Nature without the sustaining intelligence of a rational Creator who works in and through His creation?

There are no facts yet wrested from the intriguing mysteries of this strange, onrushing cosmos which can in any degree disprove the existence and intelligent activities of an unconditioned, personal God. On the contrary, when as careful scientists we analyze and synthesize the data of the natural world, even by analogical inference, we are observing only the phenomena of the operations of that unseen Being who cannot be found by mere scientific seeking, but who can and did manifest Himself in human form.

For science is indeed "watching God work."

THE INESCAPABLE CONCLUSION

BY *JOHN CLEVELAND COTHRAN*

MATHEMATICIAN AND CHEMIST

Ph.D., Cornell University; formerly on staff of Cornell University and Head of Department of Physical Science, Duluth State Teachers College; thereafter Professor of Chemistry and Chairman of Science and Mathematics Division, Duluth Branch, University of Minnesota; Lecturer in Chemistry, Kansas State Teachers College. Specialist in the preparation of ammonium trinitride and tetrazole; purification of tungsten.

LORD KELVIN, one of the world's greatest physicists, has made the following significant statement: "If you think strongly enough, you will be forced by science to believe in God." I must declare myself in full agreement with this statement.

Intelligent and informed consideration of what is presently known about the universe as a whole discloses that it must include at least three major realms of actuality. These three are the material (matter), the intellectual (mind), and the spiritual (soul).

The contribution from the field of chemistry to this consideration is necessarily limited since it is only one of many in the symposium.

Because chemistry is primarily concerned with the composition and the changes in composition of matter, along with the energy changes that accompany its changes in composition, including the interconvertibility of matter and energy, it is evidently a predominantly material and apparently an utterly un-spiritual science. How, then, can it be expected to afford any evidence of the existence of a supreme spiritual Being, God, as the Creator and Director of the universe? How can such a science be expected to help dispose of the idea that the universe owes its existence to mere chance, is ruled by chance, and that all the occurrences therein are haphazard and due only to chance?

The tremendous development that has taken place in all the physical sciences, including chemistry, during the past hundred years has resulted chiefly from the application of the "scientific method" to the study of matter and energy. In the experimental part of this study every effort is made to eliminate every known possibility that the results obtained are in any way due to mere chance. This study consistently has shown in the past, and still continues to show, that the behavior of even insensible matter is not at all haphazard, but on the contrary "obeys" definite "natural laws." Frequently the validity of a law is established long before any reason for its existence and its mode of operation has been discovered. But once the conditions are known under which it has been shown to be valid, chemists are completely confident that under those same conditions the law will continue to operate to produce the same results. They could not have this confidence if the behavior of matter and energy were haphazard and ruled by chance. And when finally the reason why the law exists, and operates as it does, has been found, even the most remote possibility of haphazardness is completely removed.

In the arrangement of the great Russian chemist, Mendelejeff, a hundred years ago (later somewhat modified and amplified), of the chemical elements in order of increasing atomic weight, could the *periodicity* of occurrence of elements possessing similar properties reasonably be ascribed to mere chance? If so, the post-prediction discovery of all of the elements whose existence he predicted, and their possession of almost exactly the properties he predicted for them, effectively removed any such possibility. His great generalization is never called "The Periodic *Chance*." Instead, it is "The Periodic *Law*."

Again, did scientists of that day ascribe to mere chance the fact that atoms of element "A" would react readily with atoms of element "B" but apparently not at all with atoms of element "C"? No. Instead they argued that there must be some sort of force or "affinity" which operated strongly between all atoms of element "A" and all atoms of element "B," but either only feebly or not at all between all atoms of element "A" and all atoms of element "C."

Again, they knew that the rate of chemical reaction of the atoms of the alkali metals with, for example, water increased with increasing atomic weight while exactly the reverse was true for atoms of the different members of the halogen family. Nobody knew the reason for this, but apparently nobody ascribed this seemingly contradictory behavior to chance or argued that perhaps next month all the different kinds of atoms would react at the same rate, or not at all, or in reverse order, or in some perfectly haphazard fashion.

The discovery of atomic structure has now revealed that in all these examples of chemical behavior definite laws prevail, not haphazardness or chance.

Consider the 102 known chemical elements and their amazing diversities and similarities. Some are colored, others are colorless; some are gases extremely difficult to liquefy and to solidify, others are already liquids, while still others are solids extremely difficult to liquefy and to vaporize; some are very soft solids, others extremely hard; some are extremely light, others extremely heavy; some are excellent conductors, others extremely poor; some are magnetic, others not; some are very reactive, others apparently totally non-reactive; some form acids, others form bases; some possess very long life, others exist for only a fraction of a second. Nevertheless all conform with the previously mentioned Periodic Law.

Yet, with all this seeming complexity, each atom of every one of the 102 elements consists of exactly the same three kinds of electrical particles: protons (positive), electrons (negative), and neutrons (each apparently some sort of combination of one proton with one electron); all the protons and neutrons of a given kind of atom are located in a central "nucleus"; all the electrons, equal in number to the protons, spin on their axes and revolve in various "orbits" about the nucleus at relatively great distances from it—rather reminiscent of a miniature solar system, so that most of the volume of the atom is merely "empty space" just as is that of the solar system. And, incredibly simplified though it may seem, the difference between an atom of one kind of element and an atom of another kind of element is due merely to the difference in the number of protons (and

[40

neutrons) in the nucleus and the number and arrangement of the electrons outside the nucleus! So that all the millions of different kinds of substances, both elements and compounds, "simplify down" to three kinds of electrical particles which, in turn, appear to be only different forms of the one primary entity, electricity, which, finally, may be only a form or attribute or manifestation of the ultimate in simplicity: energy.

Now, matter as an aggregate of molecules and atoms; the molecules and atoms themselves; their constituent protons, electrons, neutrons; electricity; energy itself—are all found to obey appropriate laws, not the dictates of chance. So true is this that 17 atoms of element 101 sufficed for its identification. The material universe is unquestionably one of system and order, not chaos; of laws, not chance and haphazards.

Can any informed and reasoning intellect possibly believe that insensible and mindless matter just chanced to originate itself and all this system, then chanced to impose the system upon itself, whereafter this system just chances to remain imposed? Surely the answer is "No!" When energy transforms into "new" matter, the transformation proceeds "according to law" and the resulting matter obeys the same laws that apply to the matter already existing.

Chemistry discloses that matter is ceasing to exist, some varieties exceedingly slowly, others exceedingly swiftly. Therefore the existence of matter is not eternal. Consequently matter must have had a beginning. Evidence from chemistry and other sciences indicates that this beginning was not slow and gradual; on the contrary, it was sudden, and the evidence even indicates the approximate time when

41]

it occurred. Thus at some rather definite time the material realm was *created* and ever since has been obeying *law*, not the dictates of chance.

Now, the material realm not being able to create itself and its governing laws, the act of creation must have been performed by some non-material agent. The stupendous marvels accomplished in that act show that this agent must possess superlative intelligence, an attribute of *mind*. But to bring mind into action in the material realm, as, for example, in the practice of medicine and in the field of parapsychology, the exercise of *will* is required, and this can be exerted only by a *person*. Hence our logical and inescapable conclusion is not only that creation occurred but that it was brought about according to the plan and will of a Person endowed with supreme intelligence and knowledge (omniscience), and the power to bring it about and keep it running according to plan (omnipotence) always and everywhere throughout the universe (omnipresence). That is to say, we accept unhesitatingly the fact of the existence of "the supreme spiritual Being, God, the Creator and Director of the universe," mentioned in the beginning of this chapter.

The advances that have occurred in science since Lord Kelvin's day would enable him to state more emphatically than ever: "If you think strongly enough, you will be forced by science to believe in God."

THE ANSWER TO THE UNANSWERED QUESTIONS

BY DONALD HENRY PORTER

MATHEMATICIAN AND PHYSICIST

B.Sc., Marion College, Ph.D., University of Indiana; formerly Teaching Fellow at University of Indiana; Professor of Mathematics and Physics at Marion College. Specialist in contact transformations, two-dimensional bounded variation and absolute continuity.

IF one could prove that there is a God in the same sense that one proves the Theorem of Pythagoras in geometry then belief in God would be compulsory. That kind of proof, I believe, does not exist. On the other hand, science is composed in the main of unproved laws or principles. This lack of proof does not prohibit one from using these laws as they might apply to various situations. It is not reasonable to expect proofs in the realm of the supernatural when proofs in the natural are lacking.

The questions in physics that can be answered best begin with the word "How." The present level of achievement in

43]

physics does not permit an answer to many questions beginning with the word "Why." The answers to "How" questions are probably only approximations to the truth. *How* two bodies attract each other is well described in Newton's Universal Law of Gravitation. An explanation of *why* two bodies attract each other does not exist. The force of gravity holds us to the earth and our earth in its orbit about the sun. But then guesswork begins. One theory of the universe requires the law of gravitation to reverse itself and the force to become one of repulsion if the distance between bodies is great enough.

There is an accepted law governing the forces between electrically charged bodies. Such charges are known as positive or negative. The law states that the force is one of attraction if the charges are of opposite sign, and of repulsion if of the same sign, the force in any case being directly proportional to the product of the charges and inversely proportional to the square of the distance between them. We believe the nucleus of an atom to contain positively charged particles called protons. But when we get into the small confines of the nucleus of an atom the law fails, and we must assume a new law of force. This law is called the "nuclear force." So even man's attempt to *describe* Nature falls short when he is dealing with the very large or the very small.

It seems that the majority of scientists feel compelled to describe physical phenomena and origins without a God in the picture. Bertrand Russell, the noted British mathematician and philosopher, decided there was no God because he could not answer the question "Who made God?" There is no doubt that Russell's thought processes went deep and far, but is it reasonable to demand an answer to this question when almost every scientific theory leads to unanswered questions? As for myself, I place God in the picture. Reason and logic demand it.

Speaking of unanswered questions, there are two theories of the universe that are receiving wide acclaim at the present. But before we take a look at them let us make some preliminary remarks.

Cosmology is the study of the general features of our universe, its extension in space and its duration in time. With the great 200-inch telescope on Mount Palomar man is able to look more than a billion light-years into space and see nearly a billion galaxies. The light-year as a unit of distance means the distance light travels in a year at 186,000 miles each second. A photograph of the heavens taken today shows the way the stars looked when the light left them, perhaps millions of years ago.

An idea that has become firmly established is that our universe is expanding. The rainbow colors one sees when looking through a glass prism are called a continuous spectrum if the colors merge together to form a continuous spread of colors. The science of spectroscopy is based on the fact that elements can be identified by their characteristic spectra. The spectrum of an element is formed by the refraction of light associated with the element into separated colors whose distribution and intensity become the fingerprints of the element. In this way an element was discovered on the sun before it was detected here on earth, and was named helium, after the Greek word *helios*, meaning sun. The shift of the spectrum toward its red end is called the red-shift and indicates that the source of the light is moving away from the observer. Observation of distant galaxies has led to the theory

45]

that the universe is expanding, that the galaxies are moving outward.

And now the two prominent theories referred to here-above. One is the evolving universe theory of Alpher and Gamow, the other is the steady-state theory of Hoyle.

According to the first theory the universe was formed by an explosion from a state of high density and temperature. It proposes that the cosmos evolved from the original, highly compressed, extremely hot gas to stars, galaxies, and background material. The present outward motion of the galaxies is a result of this explosion.

This Alpher and Gamow theory postulates that when our universe was five minutes old its temperature was a billion degrees. Before that, matter consisted only of protons, neutrons and electrons that were dissociated because of the high temperature and pressure. After the explosion, which marked the beginning of our universe, all the chemical elements were formed within thirty minutes. The theory would require the heavier elements to be combinations in successive steps of the lighter elements. There was a special time when the galaxies were formed, perhaps a million years or so after the explosion. Gravitational forces were the causative factor in the formation of the galaxies.

What about the state of affairs before the very first beginning of the universe? It is suggested that we consider the operation thuswise: that our universe came out of the maximum contraction of a previous universe that had been collapsing for an eternity of time from a state of infinite rarefaction (thinness or porousness; opposite of density).

If I should adopt the theory that our universe came from a highly compressed, very hot beginning it would be to place

God as the Creator of the original particles and the Source of the energy which brought the pressure and the heat. *God would be in the picture.*

The Bondi-Gold-Hoyle theory is called the steady-state theory, or the theory of continuous creation. It is based on the assumption that the universe is homogeneous both in space and time, but not static. Its authors agree that the universe is expanding, that the galaxies are moving outward. To compensate for the dispersal of the galaxies and still retain the same general appearance of the universe, they postulate that matter is being created continuously and forming into new galaxies to replace those moving away and out of our limit of vision by telescope. We see by light, and if a body were moving away from us with a velocity greater than the velocity of light, then light would not come toward us and vision of such a body would be impossible even with a perfect telescope. It is estimated that a galaxy two billion light-years away would have that velocity and so pass forever from our view. This is about twice the distance now expected of the giant telescope on Mount Palomar. If the universe expanded at the computed rate for about one-fifth of the estimated lifetime of the sun, the universe would become essentially empty to our observation.

The continuous creation theory would constantly replace the background material of the universe as it condensed into galaxies. Thus the general appearance of the universe would not change. The newly created material would produce an outward pressure that leads to the steady expansion. Concerning creation, Hoyle indicates that the material does not come from anywhere. It simply appears!

As for me, if I should favor the continuous creation theory,

I certainly would recognize God as the Creator. *Again God would be in the picture.*

Whatever process of Nature is considered, or whatever question of origins is studied, as a scientist I derive satisfaction only by placing God in the leading role. God is the central figure in every picture. He alone is the answer to the unanswered questions.

LET'S LOOK AT FACTS, WITHOUT BENT OR BIAS

BY EDWARD LUTHER KESSEL

ZOOLOGIST AND ENTOMOLOGIST

M.Sc., Ph.D., University of California; Professor of Biology and Chairman of the Department, University of San Francisco; on staff of California Academy of Sciences—Associate Curator of Insects; Editor of technical publications, including Wassmann Journal of Biology. Specialist in insect embryology, herpetology, salamanders, dipterology of Clythiidae.

DURING recent years scientific research has been yielding new evidence supporting the traditional philosophical proofs that there is a God. Not that this new evidence was necessary, for the old proofs were more than adequate to convince anyone whose mind was not encysted in a capsule of prejudice. But as one who already believes, I welcome these additions to the evidence for two reasons: (1) they give us a clearer concept of some of the attributes of God; (2) I am confident that they will open the eyes of many intellectually honest skeptics so that they too will see that there is a God.

49]

In late years a great religious revival has been sweeping across our nation, an upsurge in religious concern which has not bypassed our colleges but has anastomosed with the intellectual life of our higher institutions of learning. And it is certain that the new scientific evidence which points to the necessity of a Creator is playing an important role in this swing to God.

Of course the scientific research which has yielded this evidence was not planned for the purpose of proving the existence of God; the aim of science is to investigate the facts of Nature and not to concern itself about the more basic matter of origins. Science deals only with the workings of the mechanism of Nature and ignores the fundamental question of where the machine came from. But every man, even the scientist, has something of the philosopher in him, although unfortunately good scientists are not always good philosophers. Some think only vaguely about the matter of origins. Others hold the preposterous view that the universe created itself. Still others say that it is just as easy for them to suppose that the universe has always existed as to believe in a God who has always existed.

But the second law of thermodynamics (heat), or the law of entropy as it is often called, proves the last group wrong. Science clearly shows that the universe could not have existed from all eternity. The law of entropy states that there is a continuous flow of heat from warmer to colder bodies, and that this flow cannot be reversed to pass spontaneously in the opposite direction. Entropy is the ratio of unavailable to available energy, so that it may be said that the entropy of the universe is always increasing. Therefore the universe is headed for a time when the temperature will be universally uniform and there will be no more useful energy. Consequently there will be no more chemical and physical processes, and life itself will cease to exist. But because life is still going on, and chemical and physical processes are still in progress, it is evident that our universe could not have existed from eternity, else it would have long since run out of useful energy and ground to a halt. Therefore, quite unintentionally, science proves that our universe had a beginning. And in so doing it proves the reality of God, for whatever had a beginning did not begin of itself but demands a Prime Mover, a Creator, a God.

Not only do we have scientific proof that the universe has not always existed, but now science has shown that it came into existence in a single great creative explosion which began some five billion years ago. In fact, the universe is still expanding from the center of its origin. Today, those who will heed the testimony of science must believe in creation, a creation which transcends the laws of Nature, for these very laws are themselves a product of creation. And of course there could have been no such creation without a Creator, who must be equated with God. Once He had established the material of Nature, and the laws of Nature to govern its activities, He used this mechanism to continue creation— creation by evolution (evolvement, development).

I realize full well that the word *evolution* is contraband in many circles; the mere sound of it causes raised eyebrows. Strange as it may seem, I not only understand those good friends but agree with them. What they have in mind is materialistic (mechanical, or mechanistic) evolution, between which and creational evolution a sharp distinction should be drawn.

If only all scientists would consider the evidence of science here described with the same honesty and lack of prejudice with which they evaluate the results of their own research; if only they would let their intellects rule their emotions; then they would be compelled to acknowledge that there is a God. This is the only conclusion that will fit the facts. To study science with an open mind will bring one to the necessity of a First Cause, whom we call God.

God has been generous to our generation and has blessed our scientific research with many discoveries about Nature. And it is the intellectual responsibility of all men, whether scientists or not, to take account of this knowledge of science in formulating their beliefs. Just as an open-minded scientist must heed the evidence and recognize that there must be a God, the non-scientist must likewise heed the evidence and recognize that creational evolution was God's method of creation, once He had produced the material of the universe and established its laws. Creational evolution is the only explanation which correlates all of the evidence which is provided for us in the Book of Nature. Exegesis in the form of scientific research yields proof of creational evolution from every one of the chapters of this book—that of Morphology, Physiology, Embryology, Biochemistry, Genetics, Paleontology, Systematics, Zoogeography, etc.

Natural selection is one of the chief mechanisms of evolution, just as evolution is a mechanism of creation. It is one of the great laws of Nature, and like all the other laws of science it acts only as a secondary cause because it too is a product of God's creation. The species produced through natural selection are just as much created by God as if they had been manufactured by Him. Natural selection in itself cannot create anything. It merely allows or disallows the survival and reproduction of variations in Nature. These variations, from which natural selection selects, result from mutations (changes) which are the products of the laws of genetics (heredity, etc.), and these do not behave according to blind chance as the materialistic evolutionists would have us believe.

Mutations are not entirely random, or haphazard, as so many have claimed for so long. Take as an example those mutations which determine the size of organs. Recent investigations have shown that most of these mutations result in a reduction in the size of the organs concerned. Natural selection, working through blind chance on random mutations, could reduce only detrimental organs, yet it is a common observation that neutral characters are also reduced. This shows that mutations are not always random and that the mechanism of evolution is not dependent upon blind chance. We must recognize, therefore, that there is Intelligence behind its creation and in the establishment of its laws. We are forced to the conclusion that this mechanism of evolution was designed, and this demands an intelligent Designer.

Space does not permit the enumeration of other evidences of design in Nature, but I have encountered many in my own limited research in the field of insect embryology and metamorphosis. The more I study Nature, the more I am impressed with these evidences. The processes and phenomena which we observe in science are indeed manifestations of a Supreme Intelligence, and evolution merely represents a stage in creation.

In spite of the fanatical outbursts from both the camps

of fundamentalism and materialism, outbursts which have blinded many honest seekers after the truth on both sides, the conclusion that the species have been produced by an evolutionary process has in itself no negative religious significance. Quite the contrary is true—it is contradictory and illogical for one to accept the reality of evolution and not also accept the reality of God.

From the days of the great Augustine, in the fourth century, to the present there have been innumerable believers in God who have rejected the idea of creation by manufacture in favor of creation by evolution. In fact for these (and I count myself among them) evolution has a positive religious importance, leading the completely honest and unprejudiced inquirer directly to God.

Again I say that to study science with an open mind brings one to the necessity of a belief in God.

APPLYING THE SCIENTIFIC METHOD

BY WALTER OSCAR LUNDBERG

PHYSIOLOGIST AND BIOCHEMIST

Ph.D., Johns Hopkins University. Successively Physical Chemist, U.S. Steel Corporation; Professor of physiological chemistry, University of Minnesota; Professor of agricultural biochemistry, University of Minn.; Resident Director, The Hormel Institute, University of Minn. Presently, since 1949, Executive Director, The Hormel Institute. Member and past chairman and director of various national food and chemical associations. Editor of Vols. I, II, and III of "Progress in the Chemistry of Fats and Other Lipids," and author of numerous scientific articles.

THE professional scientist has one special advantage over others, if he will but use it, in understanding the reality of God. The fundamental principles on which the methodology of his profession is based, are, in essence, an expression of God's existence. Many scientists who do not recognize this point are successful as scientists, and this should not be regarded as anomalous. Success in science depends primarily on an application of accepted methodology, and does not require any searching appreciation of its fundamental principles.

55]

The failure of some scientists to understand and accept the theistic significance of the underlying principles stems from various factors, only two of which will be mentioned.

First, a denial of the existence of God is sometimes an arbitrarily established policy of influential social groups or organizations, or of the state. Fear of social consequences, or even physical consequences where atheism is a state creed, discourages any active espousal by the individual of the revelation of God found in Nature.

Again, even when the minds of men are essentially free from fear, they may not be free from other predisposing prejudices. All too frequently, in organized Christianity, there is instilled deeply in young people a concept of God created in the image of man, rather than of man created in the image of God. When such minds are later trained in science, this reversed and limiting anthropomorphic concept gradually becomes more and more incompatible with the rational, inductive attitude of science. Ultimately, when all attempts at reconciliation fail (as they frequently do because they involve rationalization processes that are in themselves inconsistent with the scientific method), the concept of God may be abandoned entirely. The accompanying disillusionment and other psychological consequences discourage any thought of embracing a new concept.

What is the scientific method, and what are the underlying principles that reveal the existence of God? In brief and oversimplified terms, the following steps will serve the purpose of this discussion:

First, the scientist observes and records selected natural phenomena. This may be done without exerting any controls over the phenomena, as in studies of stellar matter and interstellar space, or it may be done with partial controls, as in laboratory experiments.

Second, he combines his observations with observations and relationships provided by other scientists before him, and draws conclusions or develops working hypotheses. This involves inductive, rather than deductive, mental processes, inasmuch as the conclusions or hypotheses contain more than was actually observed; in essence, they are predictions.

Finally, if he wishes to test or validate his conclusions, he conducts additional and new observations, and determines if these agree with his predictions.

In short, the scientific method is founded on *orderliness* and *predictability* in natural phenomena. It is precisely this orderliness and predictability that constitute a revelation of God in Nature. Order and predictability in the framework of non-existence of God, that is, absence of rationality, is a meaningless contradiction.

The ability of man to appreciate orderliness and predictability in Nature does not necessarily follow as a consequence of the existence of God. But it *is* a consequence of the creation of man in God's image. When man abandons the concept of a God created in his image, and accepts Nature's revelations as evidence of man's creation in God's image, he has reached a threshold where he may begin to perceive God's majesty.

Man is but at the beginning of knowledge. In terms of his own physical dimensions, he has some awareness that stellar matter and interstellar space are extraordinarily vast, that the basic units of matter and energy are incomprehensibly minute, and that his own life span is but an infinitesimal fraction of a second in the timelessness of the on-going universe. He conceives dimly of the possibility of new forms and dimensions of energy, space and time, and of other such concepts as yet wholly unknown. He recognizes life as an entity but has no scientific understanding of its nature. Nevertheless, his limited understanding permits him to realize that great vistas of unexplored knowledge lie before him, based on orderliness and predictability. Therein he has a glimpse of the majesty of God.

Because man's understanding of God as revealed in natural phenomena is as yet very limited, it is in the nature of man that his belief in God should also have a spiritual basis, a basis in faith. Belief in a personal God on the basis of faith is important to personal happiness in the lives of many men. But for the scientist who believes in God there is an added satisfaction that comes with each new scientific discovery, for each discovery gives added meaning and significance to his concept of God.

PHYSICAL EVIDENCES OF GOD

BY PAUL CLARENCE AEBERSOLD

BIOPHYSICIST

A.B. cum laude, Stanford University, M.A., Ph.D., University of California. Formerly Radiation Specialist and Roentgenologist with Finney-Howell Research Foundation; Research Liaison Aide, Manhattan Project, U.S. Bureau of Standards; Director of Isotopes Division, Oak Ridge Operations, Atomic Energy Commission; presently Director for Isotopes and Radiation, Division of Civilian Application, A.E.C., Washington, D.C. Member of Committee on Nuclear Science, National Research Council, and of various national biological and radiological organizations. Specialist in nuclear physics, biophysics, properties of neutron radiation, isotopes.

FRANCIS BACON, English philosopher and statesman, said more than three centuries ago, "A little philosophy inclines man to atheism; a depth of philosophy brings him to religion."

Bacon was unquestionably right.

Millions upon millions of thinking, searching individuals throughout human existence have faced the following most profound questions: What superior Intelligence, what enor-

59]

mous Force, governs man and the universe at large? What underlies or is beyond life and human experience?

Each of the billions of persons in future generations of men—if present earth life continues—will repeat these questions. In view of the deep and multitudinous soul searching devoted to these questions we necessarily approach them humbly, without expectation of an answer that is in any way complete.

One thing is certain: even as greatly resourceful and intelligent as man is, he has never felt complete within himself. Men of different religions, races and continents have independently and universally throughout history recognized man's severe limitations in understanding and explaining the vast universe, including the most difficult question of the role and purpose of life within it.

Whether by means of intellect or spirit, the fact is that man has almost universally recognized a greater all-encompassing intelligence and order in the universe than could possibly be conceived from chance, haphazard events involving inanimate, unguided matter. That man universally accepts the need of extrapolation beyond his own intellect is in itself strong evidence for a superior Intelligence.

Unequivocal acceptance of God cannot be gained through "absolute scientific proof." Each person will finally forge his answer—the accord between his own life and God—from a molding together of his knowledge of the material and the spiritual. It will come from combining his comprehension of the infinitely expansive and complicated material universe and his inner personal responsiveness to the greatly various experiences of intellect, emotion and spirit. A census of the reasons and experiences which demonstrate God to millions

[60

of intelligent persons around the world would be infinite in variety—but also *overwhelming in total affirmation.*

Early in my scientific studies I was so enamored of human reasoning and the power of scientific methods that I felt certain that scientists could eventually explain everything in the universe—perhaps the origin of life, the derivation of the intellect, and even the meaning of everything. But as I learned more and more about everything—from atoms to galaxies, microbes to man—more and more remained unexplained. Science can go on victoriously for millennia and details of the atom, the universe as a whole, life, man and mind will still remain to be discovered. Scientists soon learn that science is limited to explaining in greater and greater detail the "how" of things. But neither science nor man can explain the "why." Science, human reasoning alone, will never explain why there are atoms, stars, galaxies, life and man with all his marvelous capacities. Although science can develop very plausible theories of a cataclysmic birth of the universe resulting in galaxies, stars, worlds and atoms, it cannot explain where all this matter and energy came from and why the universe is so constituted and ordered. Straight thinking, clear reasoning demand the concept of God.

Is God a "personal" God, as many conceive Him to be? From a viewpoint of science, I do not think of Him as "personal" in the sense that He sits on a throne somewhere like a human king. The sacred writings, in describing God and His nature, made ample use of figures of speech derived from human life and human history. God, being a spiritual Being, could not be described in purely spiritual terms, because man as a dichotomous, earthbound being would not have been able to employ such terms or comprehend them.

61]

On the other hand, God in His spirituality and transcendence has moral virtues, the capacity for thought, volition and feeling, and in that sense He is an objective, personal Being. In fact, He is the Divine Prototype of which our human personalities are faint and finite copies. That is what is meant by the statement that man is the "image of God."

God is in no sense physical. For that reason He is beyond our human capacity to describe or explain Him in a physical sense. At the same time there are abundant physical evidences of His existence, and His works prove Him to be infinite in wisdom, knowledge and power. But God being unfathomable, man cannot fathom the ultimate purpose of himself or the great universe of which he—physically—is such a microscopically small and insignificant part.

The one thing we all certainly realize is that man and the universe did not spring forth spontaneously from absolutely nothing. They had a beginning, and there was a Beginner. We also realize that the marvelous and intricate physical order of the universe follows laws not dictated by man, and that the miracle of life itself has an origin and a guidance beyond man—a Divine origin and a Divine guidance.

IDENTIFYING EINSTEIN'S "CREATIVE FORCE"

BY MARLIN BOOKS KREIDER

PHYSIOLOGIST

M.Sc., Ph.D., University of Maryland. Physiologist with Environmental Protection Division, U.S. Quartermaster's Research and Development Center, Natick, Mass.; also Professor of Biology, Eastern Nazarene College. Member of American Society of Professional Biologists, National Speleological Society, etc. Specialist in metabolism and circulation.

BOTH as an ordinary human being, and also as a man devoting his life to scientific study and research, I have no doubt at all about the existence of God.

There is, definitely, a God.

But His existence cannot be proved, nor can He in any way be analyzed, by laboratory methods. He is non-physical. He is a spiritual, intelligent, creative, all-sustaining Power.

But though we cannot use ordinary scientific methods in determining His existence, yet we can study the manifold evidences of His existence in man and in Nature at large. Those evidences, to my mind, are clear-cut and convincing.

May I state here that many of the so-called theories or facts of science that many people assume to be true are also not proven facts. Many of them are merely indications pointing in the direction of facts, instead of established verities. It's something like a man that you see running out of the back door of your house which you discover has been ransacked. You do not have proof that he is guilty, but evidence certainly points in that direction. A magistrate weighs the evidence before the proof of guilt is established.

In addition, the scientific method is inadequate to demonstrate or prove the existence of *every* reality. For example, love, undeniably one of the strongest forces affecting man, can defy scientific proof or analysis. Likewise, how can beauty or the appreciation of music be proved to someone lacking appreciation? But who would deny their existence? Evidences of the existence of God equally as strong as those often accepted as proof in many fields of rational, scientific thought can be found, even though conclusive proof for or against the existence of God may be lacking.

Our first body of evidence is found in cosmology, in the existence of a universe which is governed by precise forces of Nature and an orderliness which suggests an arranger or organizer. This precision is so great that the path of planets and, more recently, the artificial satellites can be predicted in advance. This preciseness extends to the interaction of electric charges involved in chemical reactions. It allows most physical phenomena to be expressed by mathematical law and formula. Such order, according to common human experience, is a result of an orderly mind. Chaos rather than order emerges unless a designing or controlling force is functioning.

Another group of evidences lies in the realm of life and organic structure. Of special interest to the writer as a physiologist is the intricacy of design and structure of the human and animal bodies. The creation or construction of any one organ of the body is far beyond the ability of the most ingenious man, though the function of some structures can be reproduced to a very limited degree by artificial devices. Among these are the artificial lung, heart, kidney and mechanical brain.

Speaking of the brain, that possesses unbelievable abilities, yet little more is known of its physical basis than that it can initiate and conduct electric-like charges and that some chemical changes take place. But its numerous functions—who can explain or account for them? It is responsible for co-ordinating all muscular activities and controls even the most basic bodily functions such as respiration and heart beat. It contains memory, and holds thousands of mental images available for instant recall. Is there any physical explanation of the integrating and problem-solving ability of the brain, or of reason and common sense, of motivation, desire, and serenity? The appreciation of an aesthetic quality such as beauty, the comprehension of a spiritual reality such as love, the consciousness of self, personality development—all are functions of this same small mass of protoplasm. But who can explain them on a physical basis—or even at all?

Among the many complexities of the body is the intricate control of the myriad chemical reactions continually taking place, some of which cannot be duplicated outside of the body. The buffer systems which neutralize the acids of digestion and of exercise maintain the optimum conditions for metabolism. Antibodies form to fight off harmful invaders

65]

and may confer immunity. These antibodies are specific for each disease, just as the structure of the chemicals composing the protoplasm is specific for each individual. Each human being therefore possesses a chemical distinctness. Who was it that brought this about? Certainly not mere man!

And think of the heart. This tireless organ responds to ceaseless demands throughout a lifetime. It also possesses a mysterious rhythmicity which allows it to beat even though all nerve attachments are severed—a highly important fact in cases of accident. Where do we go with this perpetual physical miracle? How do we explain it?

These marvels of bodily function are very closely associated with the mystery of life itself, a mystery that scientists and philosophers have long wrestled with—long, but vainly. Much is known about the characteristics of living protoplasm and of the intricate chemical reactions continuously taking place, but we lack adequate, thoroughgoing definitions. There is a theory called vitalism, which suggests that there is some force in addition to the known physical forces necessary for life, but, in the first place, the theory is held in disrepute by many scientists, and secondly, it too does not explain the real essence of life, nor does it explain by known and measured phenomena the direction and purposefulness that is apparent in the growth and development of every living organism. What is the organizing and directive force in embryological growth that causes a small mass of undifferentiated cells finally to produce the complex arrangement of adult tissue?

At this point we must face the realization that we dare not equate all that we do not understand to God's special intervention as did the primitive peoples who considered storm and thunder signs of God's displeasure. However, this purposefulness found in life and growth points definintely to order and design.

Turning to another area, in cosmogony, the study of the origination of the universe, we find additional evidence of a creative, extra-mundane force. It has been proposed that the first solid matter was formed from the interaction of hot swirling gases which grew to larger dimensions and split into smaller masses. These smaller masses were flung into space, finally forming the array of heavenly bodies. In similar manner, it has been proposed, life was formed. However, since the time of Pasteur it has been an accepted scientific fact that life does not arise from non-living matter, thus contradicting this theory of origins. In addition, our laboratories with their elaborate equipment for reproducing great varieties of environmental conditions have succeeded in creating some components of protoplasm, but not life. The mathematical probability of a chance occurrence of all the necessary factors in the right proportion is almost nil.

Even if some substance *were* created in this manner, there still remains the question of the origin of the initial element or electrical charges, the heat, and the physical forces which kept the newly formed masses suspended and moving, and which are now controlling the physical universe.

This view of creation also creates other problems. If life began as a small mass of protoplasm, an elaborate force must have acted upon it to produce the vast variety of living structures inhabiting the earth. When known scientific mechanisms are examined by which organic evolution of a mass of protoplasm could form the complex man of today, they are found inadequate.

In the first place, the science of genetics reveals a few types of alteration of the gene, but there is no evidence that these alterations could account for any great complexity of structure. Secondly, the law of the survival of the fittest suggests that some change takes place, but cannot explain the development of the many varieties or species of animals and plants. Furthermore, the study of entropy, or the available energy of the universe, reveals a continual decrease from an initial point. This is in the opposite direction required for organic evolution of simple protoplasm to complex man.

Obviously no one in our present intellectual state will ever have proof of the method involved in creation. But our scientific knowledge reveals so many improbabilities in the completely materialistic explanation that it is more rational to accept as the prime cause a form of special creation and the influence of an outside force. Albert Einstein, in recognizing this intelligent creative force, refers to it as "the illimitable superior reasoning power which is revealed in the incomprehensible universe."

As stated at the outset, I call this "power" God.

I see at the beginning of the cosmic road—not eternal energy or matter, not "inscrutable fate," not a "fortuitous conflux of primordial elements," not "the great Unknown" —but the Lord God Almighty.

And I do not consider my position "irrational."

Mortal men whose reach and ken is so extremely limited, as I have tried to point out in very brief compass, might do well not to bank too much on their "ratio"—calling this ratio-nal, and that ir-ratio-nal.

In any event, here is where I stand, and this is my belief.

SCIENTIFIC REVELATIONS
POINT TO A GOD

BY GEORGE EARL DAVIS

PHYSICIST

M.S., Iowa State College, Ph.D., University of Minnesota; formerly physicist Naval Ordnance Laboratory; since 1948 Head of Nucleonics Section, Material Laboratory, N.Y. Naval Shipyard, Brooklyn; specialist in spectrophotometry, solar radiation, geometrical and physical optics.

As knowledge increases and old superstitions come to be recognized for what they are, a more critical evaluation of the tenets of religion and theology is inevitable.

The motives behind such re-evaluation may be various. But we must assume that they spring from a real desire to know the truth. We must guard against the error of confusing agnosticism and atheism, and we must recognize that he who attacks only the traditional bases for belief in a Supreme Being does not, because of that alone, deserve the stigma of "atheist." Such a one may also believe in the existence of a God and may, in fact, rest that belief on a firm base.

That atheism exists in scientific circles is undeniable. But

69]

the popular belief that atheism is more prevalent among scientists than among the unscientific has never been proved and is, in fact, contrary to the impressions gained at first hand by many of the scientists themselves.

As to my own belief in a Supreme Being, it would be foolish to state that it is not influenced by my early teaching. We never quite escape from religious instruction received in our formative years. But I can say with certainty that my present belief, while in agreement with that which I was taught as to the existence of a God, has a firm basis which is quite distinct from that of ecclesiastical authority.

As a physicist, I have had the privilege of seeing something of the unbelievably complex structure of the universe, in which the internal vibrations of the smallest atom are no less wonderful than the tremendous activity of the greatest star; where every ray of light, every physical and chemical reaction, every characteristic of every living thing, comes into being and runs its course in obedience to the same immutable laws. This is the picture science has unfolded, and the longer one examines it the more intricate and beautiful it becomes.

But with the marvelous revelations of scientific research have come inevitable questions, not new but brought into new perspective by clearer insight into the fabric of the universe, of which the human race is revealed as an inextricable part. One of these questions, of vital importance because of its inferences with respect to our moral responsibilities and ultimate destiny, is the old question, "Is there a God, a Supreme Being who created the universe?"; and with it there is the still more difficult question, asked by many young children in an amazing and disconcerting flash of reasoning, "If God made us, who made God?"

It is undeniable that there is no real scientific proof either that there is or is not a God. It is even quite possible that no strictly scientific proof ever can be formulated. We live in a physical universe that is, so far as the most penetrating research has been able to discover, perfectly consistent in its structure and its laws. But there is no reason to believe that it can give us information concerning anything outside of itself. It may well be a room without windows, or with windows transparent only to eyes that look in, not out.

Since we cannot prove the existence or non-existence of a God, then the best we can do is to make intelligent inferences from what we know. Such an inference, which cannot be logically attacked on the basis of any knowledge available to us, is this: *No material thing can create itself.*

If a universe could create itself, then it would embody in itself the powers of a Creator, a God, and we should be forced to conclude that the universe itself is a God. Thus the existence of a God would be admitted, but in the peculiar form of a God that is both supernatural and material. I choose to conceive of a God who has created a material universe not identical with himself but dominated and permeated by himself.

To this I add a second inference: *The higher the evolutionary developments to which a creation leads, the stronger the evidence of a supreme intelligence behind that creation.*

The evolutionary developments in our universe, so convincingly demonstrated by science, are our evidence. From a universe of elementary particles, "without form and void," have come the billions of stars and perhaps greater billions of planets, definite in form, definitely describable, living out their inevitable lives under immutable laws that somehow, with an artifice probably forever beyond mortal comprehension, were built into each of the infinitesimal particles of which they were formed.

This is evidence enough. But to it we must add the greatest miracle of all, that into those original, exceedingly minute particles were built all the principles that were necessary to evolve not only stars and planets but myriad forms of living things as well, even creatures who can think and aspire and create intricate and lovely things, and finally, in a glorious demonstration of intellectual godlikeness, pierce into the very mysteries of life itself. Edward Fitzgerald has beautifully described this supreme miracle of creation in his immortal *Rubaiyat* from the great Persian astronomer:

> With Earth's first Clay They did the Last Man knead,
> And there of the Last Harvest sowed the Seed:
> And the first Morning of Creation wrote
> What the Last Dawn of Reckoning shall read.

These revelations of transcendent intelligence behind the evolution of the universe are, for me, sufficient evidence of a God. They are sufficient even without the inference that no material thing can create itself.

PLAIN WATER WILL TELL YOU THE STORY

BY THOMAS DAVID PARKS

RESEARCH CHEMIST

Ph.D., University of Illinois. Formerly Chairman Department of Chemistry, Stanford Research Institute; at present Director of Research, Clorox Chemical Company. Specialist in microchemistry, electrolytic phenomena, X-ray diffraction and synthetic resins.

WHITTAKER CHAMBERS in his book *Witness* tells of a simple incident which was probably the turning point of his life (and perhaps of the affairs of mankind). He was watching his little daughter and unconsciously became aware of the shape of her ears. He thought to himself how impossible that such delicate convolutions could have come about by chance. They could have been created only by pre-meditated design. But he pushed this thought out of his agnostic mind because he realized that the next step in logical sequence would have to be: design presupposes God —a thesis he was not yet ready to accept.

I have known many scientists among my professors and

73]

fellow research workers who have had similar thoughts about observed facts in chemistry and physics, even though they have not spoken from the depths of despair that Whittaker Chambers found himself in.

I see order and design all about me in the inorganic world. I cannot believe that they are there by the haphazard, fortunate coming together of atoms. For me this design demands an intelligence, and this intelligence I call God.

Probably to a chemist the periodic arrangement of the elements is the most arresting. One of the first things a freshman chemistry student learns is the periodicity or order found in the elements. This order has been variously described and classified but we usually credit Mendeleev, the Russian chemist of the last century, with our periodic table. Not only did this arrangement provide a means of studying the known elements and their compounds but it also gave impetus to the search for those elements which had not yet been discovered. Their very existence was postulated by vacant spaces in the orderly arrangement of the table.

Chemists today still use the periodic table to aid them in their study of reactions and to predict properties of unknown or new compounds. That they have been successful is sound testimony to the fact that beautiful order exists in the inorganic world.

But the order we see around us is not a relentless omnipotence. It is tempered with beneficence—a testimony to the fact that good and pleasure are as much a concern of Divine Intelligence as the immutable laws of Nature. Look around you at the exceptions and deviations that do, in fact, defy the laws of cold rationality.

Take, for example, water. From its formula weight—18—one would predict it would be a gas at ordinary temperatures and pressures. Ammonia—with a formula weight of 17—is a gas at temperatures as low as minus 33° C. at atmospheric pressure. Hydrogen sulfide, closely related to water by position in the periodic table and with a formula weight of 34, is a gas at temperatures down to minus 59° C. The fact that water exists as a liquid at all, at ordinary temperatures, is something to make one stop and think.

Water has many other properties, however, which are interesting and which taken together are to me strong evidence of design. On a gross scale it should be pointed out that water covers about three-quarters of our planet, Earth, and as such exerts a tremendous influence on the temperatures and weather conditions which prevail. One can imagine catastrophic variations in temperature if water did not have a unique combination of properties. Water has a high heat of melting, a long period of liquidity, and a very high heat of vaporization. As such, it is a wonderful shock absorber to changes in temperature. In other words, without the built-in resistance to temperature which water exhibits, this earth would be much less suitable for life and much less pleasant for human activity.

There are other unique properties of water which appeal to me as having been designed by a Creator who has concern for His creatures. Water is the only known substance which becomes lighter as it freezes. This is tremendously important to life. Because of it, ice floats instead of sinking to the bottom of lakes and rivers and gradually forming a solid mass. On the top of the water it forms a layer of insulation to maintain the water below at a temperature above freezing. Fish and other marine life are preserved and the ice melts rapidly in the spring.

Other very interesting properties of this common substance, water, could be pointed out. For example, it has a high surface tension which aids in plant growth by transporting nutrients through the soil. It has a high dialetric constant which makes it the best solvent known and as such plays a vital role in the life processes of our bodies as a principal constituent of our blood. It has a high vapor pressure over a very wide range of temperature and still remains liquid throughout the whole range needed for life.

Many scientists have studied these amazing properties of water and have developed theories to account for the phenomena observed. But even if we learn to understand the "How" of the whole subject, we still must search for an answer to the "Why." And water is not the only marvelous substance! There are any number of other substances with properties so nearly sensational that our finite human mind cannot but halt—and quietly genuflect in wonderment.

Personally, I have found my explanation of these marvels —a satisfying explanation—in relating Nature's order to a Supreme Intelligence and its design to a Supreme Designer, and in it all I see more than cold, rational planning—I see the concern and love of a Creator for His creatures.

NATURE'S COMPLEXITY AND GOD

BY JOHN WILLIAM KLOTZ

GENETICIST

Ph.D., University of Pittsburgh, B.D., Concordia Seminary. Professor of biology, physiology and Nature study, Concordia Teachers College, since 1945. Member of Genetics Association. Specialist in genetics of habrobracon and mormoniella, ecology, lethals, semi-lethals, etc.

In considering the subject in hand two ancient sacred affirmations at once come to mind:

The heavens declare the glory of God and the firmament showeth His handiwork.

The fool hath said in his heart, There is no God.

This world of ours is so complex and so intricate that it could hardly have risen by chance. It is filled with intricacies which require as their cause an Intelligent Being, not blind fate. Science has certainly contributed to our understanding and appreciation of these intricacies, and in that way adds to and aids our natural knowledge of God.

Some of the most interesting of these intricacies are the

various obligate relationships. One of the best known of these is the relationship between the yucca moth and the yucca plant, or Spanish bayonet. The yucca flower hangs down, and the pistil, or female part of the flower, is lower than the stamen, or male part. The stigma, however, the part of the flower specialized for the reception of pollen, is cup-shaped, and so arranged that it is impossible for the pollen to fall into it. Instead, the pollen must be transported by the female of the yucca moth who begins her work soon after sunset. She collects a quantity of pollen from the anthers of the plants and holds it in her specially constructed mouth parts. Then she flies to another yucca flower, pierces the ovary with her ovipositor, and after laying one or more eggs creeps down the style and stuffs the ball of pollen into the stigma. The plant produces a large number of seeds. Some are eaten by the larvae of the moth and some mature to perpetuate the plant.

A similar situation exists in the relationship between the commercial fig and a group of small wasps. Two kinds of flower clusters are produced, one containing both male and female flowers, the other only female flowers. Both are pollinated by the female wasps. The openings into these flower clusters are so nearly closed by overlapping scales that the wasps can get into them only with great difficulty. Usually in the process they tear off their wings. After entering a cluster containing both male and female flowers, the female wasp lays her eggs and dies. These eggs hatch and the young wasps mate. Only the female wasps are able to leave the flower cluster. The male wasps die. Before leaving, the female becomes dusted with pollen which she carries to another flower cluster. If this cluster contains both male and female flowers the process is repeated. But if it contains only female flowers, she dies without laying her eggs, for in this case the female flowers are so long that she cannot get to the base of them to lay her eggs. In her attempt to do so, however, she dusts these flowers with pollen, and they mature to produce the ripe figs. When figs were first introduced into the United States, they did not produce the fruit. It was only after the wasp was brought in that it was possible to develop a commercially profitable fig industry.

Very unusual are the prison flowers, such as the common jack-in-the-pulpit. This plant has two kinds of flower clusters, male and female. These are produced inside the pulpit which has a constriction about half way down. Usually pollination is effected by a tiny fly which comes in, gets past the constriction, and then finds himself trapped. Not only is the constriction in his way, but the sides of the pulpit are also waxy, preventing his getting a foothold. And so he buzzes around frantically, dusting himself with pollen in the process. Shortly thereafter the sides of the pulpit roughen, and he is able to crawl out, covered with pollen. If he visits next another male cluster, the process is repeated. But if he comes into a female flower, it is possible that he will not escape. For his frantic buzzing dusts the flower with pollen, and this time the plant is not interested in his escaping. It is to the plant's advantage to have him escape from the male pulpit to carry the pollen with him. The plant seems unconcerned, however, about his escape from a female flower.

All of these instances testify to the existence of God. It is hard to believe that these could have arisen by blind chance: their existence is due to God's directing hand and to His creative power.

And we can see further evidence of this in the many instances where man to his regret has attempted to make changes in the balance of Nature, only to upset it.

When the early settlers came to Australia they found no placental mammals there except the dingo, or wild dog. Having come from Europe, they remembered the fine hunting provided by the rabbit there. And so in an attempt to improve Nature Thomas Austin imported some 24 European rabbits, back in 1859. The results were unfortunate, for there were no natural enemies in Australia to keep the rabbits in check. They multiplied beyond all expectation and did serious damage, destroying the grass on which the sheep fed. At first an attempt was made to control them by building 7,000 miles of rabbit-proof fences across the continent in Queensland, but this proved useless, for the rabbits got through them. Then an attempt was made to reduce their numbers by a system of bounties, but also this effort proved unsuccessful. Only in recent years has a solution been found, and this is the introduction of a virus disease, myxomatosis, which kills the rabbits and keeps their numbers in check. Even this may not be the final answer, for we are now beginning to hear of virus-resistant rabbits in Australia. Yet even the present reduction in their numbers has had its distinct benefits. Prairies once ravaged by erosion and hills grazed to the soil for decades are now miraculously clothed with green. During 1952–53 the sheep industry alone showed an increased productivity worth about $84,000,000.

It is possible that we may have a similar rabbit problem here in the United States. The European rabbit is a different species from our native rabbit. It is known in the United States only on San Juan Island, off the coast of Washington, where it has flourished in isolation since 1900. Recently some well intentioned sportsmen's clubs have attempted to introduce this European, or San Juan, form into various parts of the United States because it has no longer been possible to import the cottontail from state to state as was formerly done. The result could very easily be disastrous, since the San Juan rabbit might multiply as rapidly in this country as it has in Australia. One attempt to combat this was the recent decision of one state game commission to lift all bans on hunting the San Juan rabbit. It may now be hunted all the year round.

It is interesting to note that the introduction of rabbit virus into Europe has had its effect there. A French doctor, concerned about the damage that rabbits were doing to his shrubbery, imported a culture of the virus and injected it into a few rabbits that he had trapped. These were then released. The result has been a reduction in the rabbit population in France and the neighboring countries of Europe. What the total effect has been is still being debated. There has been a loss of a meat supply which was formerly available to the common people and on which they depended. Others report that this loss has been more than offset by the increase in garden crops.

A moment ago instances were mentioned testifying to the *existence* of God. What has been described just now is a powerful testimony to God's *wisdom*. The balances which He has established are delicate, and man interferes with them at the risk of doing considerable damage. Man also should be very hesitant to try to *improve* Nature's balances—he will find that his human intelligence is no match for that of Nature's God.

THE MOST VITAL QUESTION
CONFRONTING US

BY OSCAR LEO BRAUER

PHYSICIST AND CHEMIST

M.Sc., Ph.D., University of California. Professor of physics and chemistry, San Jose State College of California, since 1926. Specialist in organic chemistry, rate of reaction of cinchonine into cinchotoxin, soil analysis for phosphorus, etc.

It is the belief of this writer that the origin of things is the most vital question confronting us. Any philosophy of life stands or falls according to its explanation of the beginning of things as we find them.

Let's take a look at the planet we live on, Earth. No one in his right mind would deny its existence, nor that of the rest of the immense sidereal universe. So we're dealing with an object that is unquestionably *real*.

The earth has an incomprehensibly large mass, namely 6,600 billion times billion tons. It is a question whether the human mind can comprehend one million, let alone a billion, or a billion times billion. The day laborer at the end of the day used to exclaim, "Another day another dollar, a million days a million dollars." Little did he realize that a million days would be 2,742 years, with no vacations.

From whence came all this mass that we call Earth?

And then consider the masses of the other planets in our solar system. The sun, by far the largest member of this system, has a mass 330,000 times the 6,600 billion billion tons of the earth. In our galaxy there are at least a billion suns, the average mass of which is considerably greater than that of our sun. Leading astronomers tell us with the utmost assurance that there are at least one hundred thousand galaxies similar to ours. In any event, there are an almost countless number of immense celestial bodies. How many tons of mass is represented in all this? The mere thought is dizzying, stupefying. And how did all this mass, how did these unnumbered colossal heavenly bodies originate? There are only two possible answers: either they have existed from eternity, or they were created.

In the case of the first answer we are dealing with a false hypothesis. Among the fundamental properties or characteristics of things material are those of change, growth, and development. Natural science points definitely to a beginning of things. In the case of the second answer—creation—opinions all through the ages have differed widely. The theories, conceptions and beliefs concerning the creational origin of the universe can readily be grouped under five heads:

First, there is mythology. That of course is purely the product of human imagination. Still, even mythology indicates that there is something in the human spirit that pulls man back to the aboriginal truth that extra-human, that Divine Power made the cosmos.

Second, there is tradition. That represents stories and accounts of the events of creation that have been handed down from one generation to another. Though these accounts are badly garbled, yet they frequently contain material that reminds one strongly of the Genesis report.

Third, there is philosophy. Keen thinkers among men adopt and work out hypotheses about the origin of things. If these hypotheses find response among many other thinkers, they become popular, and in halls of learning throughout the world they are accepted as the reliable results of scientific learning and investigation. Hosts of minor scholars and teachers follow.

Fourth, there are the physical and biological sciences. These deal with the hard facts of man and Nature as we know them. They investigate, dissect, compare—take their scalpels and high-power lenses down into the embryonic, most rudimentary forms of material existence; they measure and calculate, and with their delicate, complicated, huge instruments soar into vast, almost limitless heights; they study Nature's history and laws and modes of operation; and in this and other ways seek to find out the factual truths about the origin of things.

Fifth, there is Special Divine Revelation. Another name for that is the Bible. Science can establish that a creative act at some time must have taken place, implying the existence of a Divine Intelligence and a Divine Power. Science can also establish that none but a Divine Intelligence could have been the Author of the tremendous, involved and intricate system of laws in the universe. But only the Bible can identify that Divine Intelligence and Power as the God most of us have learned to know about from early childhood—the God who has revealed himself uniquely and supremely in His Son, Jesus Christ.

Returning to our discussion of the immense size of the

universe and the incalculable multitude and mass of stars and planets, and thinking of the multiplicity of laws that govern these stars and planets, as well as animate and inanimate creatures on earth—does it not seem passing strange that our communist fellowmen, constituting as they do a large segment of the human race, reject the idea that there is a God? Does it not seem equally strange that a large fraction of the educated people in the non-communist world practically repudiate God by ignoring Him?

General recognition of God as Creator—and hence Sovereign—of the universe would mean, for one thing, an end to man's inhumanity to man. It would mean a new spirit in man, a sensitive conscience, a purified judgment. It would mean love and righteousness.

Atheism means strife and war. As a scientist I will have none of it. I consider it illogical and false, as a theory. In its practical aspects I consider it disastrous.

RANK MATERIALISM WILL NOT DO

BY IRVING WILLIAM KNOBLOCH

NATURAL SCIENTIST

M.A., University of Buffalo, Ph.D., Iowa State College. Formerly wildlife technician with U.S. Fish and Wildlife Service; since 1945 Professor of the Natural Sciences, Michigan State University. Specialist in cytology of plants, morphology, agrostology.

SCIENTISTS who are "carried away" by the inherent possibilities in their subject are wont to look upon science as potentially able to solve all problems. Life to them is nothing but an expression of the operation of chemical and physical laws. Phenomena formerly attributed to supernatural forces have been properly placed, one by one, in a known cause-and-effect relationship. There is no purpose in the universe, and in obedience to the second law of thermodynamics (heat mechanics) all will end, in a cold and silent fade-out, when the supply of fuel in our solar system has been spent.

This extreme materialistic view of Nature was summed up by Bertrand Russell who said, "That man is the product of causes which have no pre-vision of the end they are achieving; that his origin, his growth, his hopes and fears, his loves and beliefs are but the outcome of accidental collocations of atoms; that no fire, no heroism, no intensity of thought and feeling, can preserve an individual beyond the grave; that all the labors of the ages, all the devotion, all the inspiration, all the noonday brightness of human genius, are destined to extinction in the vast death of the solar system, and that the whole temple of man's achievement must inevitably be buried beneath the débris of a universe in ruins—all these things, if not quite beyond dispute, are yet so nearly certain, that no philosophy which rejects them can hope to stand."

Not all scientists, however, feel that science is omnipotent; that it can measure or account for everything; that it can assay truth, beauty, or happiness. Science cannot explain life. Science cannot discover the purpose of life. It also can never really prove that God exists or does not exist.

Science deals with the improvement of its theories. It attempts to approach reality and truth but these, like the will-o'-the-wisp, retreat as the probing continues. Our impressions of the universe are based upon our imperfect senses and upon the tools which we have, relatively speaking, clumsily fashioned. In this connection it is interesting to note that the famous American physician and essayist, Oliver Wendell Holmes, once said that as knowledge advances, science ceases to frown upon religion. Science, properly understood, is making it more and more possible to believe in a Supreme Being.

Science has no adequate explanation for the origin of the many sub-microscopic particles of matter known to exist. It cannot explain, solely upon the laws of chance, how atoms and molecules could have come together to form life. The

87]

theory which states dogmatically that all higher forms of life have evolved to their present state by chance mutations, recombinations, polyploidy or hybridization, requires an act of faith for adherence to it, an act of unreasoned acceptance.

Yes, science demands faith—faith in the senses, faith in instrumentation, faith in authority and faith in probability, or chance. In a certain sense it can be said that here, in faith, science and religion stand upon common ground, although there is this difference that science can, within its own province, check its beliefs by observation and experimentation. By its continual self-criticism it tends to eliminate the possibility of error.

Religious faith is bolstered, fortified by scientific discoveries. Enough verification, by science, of Biblical statements has occurred to "renew our strength" (Isaiah), and we may reasonably assume that more revelations will be substantiated. Astronomy points to a beginning in the far distant past and physics foretells an ultimate doom. From a standpoint of modern science it is unreasonable to assume that the universe always existed, or that it always will exist. Change is one of the primary characteristics of the universe, and in this regard science and religion agree.

As stated above, science can never actually prove the existence of God, or explain Him. Yet the wonders of the universe have converted many neutral astronomers to the belief that someone unknown, and perhaps unknowable, has been responsible for the vastness and order so apparent. Chad Walsh once said: "All that can be asked of anyone, theist or atheist, is that he show the balance of probability to be on his side." That of course is a rather flippant way of putting it; a rather whimsical approach to the problem.

Thomas Miller Forsyth had a sounding line that reached deep and far: "Anything that can be known by the finite or human mind concerning the existence and nature of God must be the outcome of man's experience of God. The experience must come first; the knowledge can only be an interpretation of the experience."

As for myself, I do not rebel, as a scientist, at the laws of chance because I see them operating at many levels in our everyday lives. I do not reject materialism in toto because scientists are only successful when they attempt natural explanations of difficult phenomena.

But I believe in God. I believe in Him because I do not think that mere chance could account for the emergence of the first electrons or protons, or for the first atoms, or for the first amino acids, or for the first protoplasm, or for the first seed, or for the first brain. I believe in God because to me His Divine existence is the only logical explanation for things as they are.

A PERSONAL GOD, VIEWED SCIENTIFICALLY

BY JOHN LEO ABERNETHY

RESEARCH CHEMIST

M.Sc., Ph.D., Northwestern University; has taught at Humboldt State College and California State Polytech. College; now Professor of Chemistry, Fresno State College, California; Associate Editor, Journal of Chemical Education. Specialist in unsaturated compounds of a conjugate nature, carbohydrates, orientation influences in the halogenation of substituted biphenyls.

IN our modern times we have developed a razor-sharp approach in solving problems, once they become clearly defined and meaningful. We have also learned that semantics, or the meaning of words, depends upon our five sensory experiences, namely taste, touch, smell, sound and sight. Each of us must necessarily live in at least moderately different environments. Hence, in extreme cases the word "house" might mean a cave to people on the outskirts of Chihuahua City or a castle on a hillside to a newspaper tycoon in California.

The question "Is there a God?" ought to be answered in

terms of the meaning of the word God. Let me venture to suggest that if by this term we mean only the law and order of the universe, then we are talking about the same thing that the communists believe in. They believe in the law and order of the universe. But they also recognize that you can pray forever to the periodic table of the elements and none of those elements, independently or in combination, could by themselves lift one finger to answer such a prayer, regardless of how psychologically self-inspiring that prayer might be. Neither do I mean the God of fantasy of nearly all the world's great religions.

The only God in whom I can have a grain of confidence is the God of the Hebrew-Christian faith—the only personal God who could possibly be interested in each one of us on this minute speck of the universe we call Earth.

Is this God real or a myth? Did He ever make himself known in the mainline stream of man's history on the earth? These questions hinge on the question "Was Christ more than a man?" The manner in which we coordinate our thoughts concerning the universe depends on how we answer this latter question. We can use the same scientific method in including or excluding a personal God.

If I take the position that Christ was merely a human being and the miraculous events written about Him were myths, then I may reasonably construct a universe based on sensory experiences and make daring guesses as to how the universe is constituted. The scientific method combines the deductive logic of Aristotle (B.C. 335) with the inductive logic of Sir Francis Bacon (A.D. 1620), as subsequently modified by men of science. In deductive logic I go from a major premise and a minor premise to a conclusion. For instance, all neutral carbon atoms contain six electrons; this is a neutral carbon atom; therefore, this atom contains six electrons. In inductive logic I go from facts to laws to hypotheses (which contain postulates, or inabsolute scientific truths).

If deductions from these "truths" turn out to be reasonable, a hypothesis rests on firmer ground and is consequently often named a theory. Knowable facts are statements of results of reproducible, sensory experiences (or in a formal or scientific sense, experiments). For instance, it is a fact that water is composed of 11.1 percent hydrogen and 88.9 percent oxygen, because various experiments can reproduce these results. Laws are generalizations of known facts. The law of definite composition, for instance, generalizes that every pure compound (water, table salt, and cane sugar) contains the same percentage composition of its constituent elements by weight.

Theories are mental pictures that explain known laws. Our chief theories that dominate modern thought are the kinetic molecular theory, the atomic theory, the theory of evolution, the theory of relativity, and the quantum theory. The atomic theory originally was based on the law of definite composition and the law of multiple proportions. The inabsolute truths of Dalton's (1806) original theory (or hypothesis) had to be modified when the atom was found to be divisible into sub-atomic particles (electrons, neutrons, etc.), and when isotopes (as heavy and light hydrogen) were discovered.

Theories lead on to systematically organized bodies of knowledge called sciences. An integration of sciences that relates man to his universe is called a philosophy. If Christianity is taken to be largely mythical, a philosophy could become materialistic—perhaps involving a finite, expanding universe, or something closely akin to this. Good and evil would have no absolute meaning; just because you or I call something good doesn't make it so. Man's behavior would be neutral, just as that of any other animal, or any plant.

Now, I choose to take Christianity as genuine. To be sent from God, Christ must present an authentic passport of identification, namely His virgin birth. A little experimentation with deductive logic would establish Him as an odd product of evolution, undoubtedly illegitimately born, if this is not so. He gave evidence, through reproducible experiences of many witnesses, that He was the Son of God, not just by a good life, but by healing the blind, feeding the multitudes, being raised from the dead, and ascending into Heaven with a promise of return, thus rightfully claiming "I am the way, the truth and the life; no man cometh unto the Father but by Me."

This being so, there is every reason to believe that God is love, and that He is a spirit (John 4: 24). But a spirit does not have flesh and bones (Luke 24: 39). If you were God, trying to explain spiritual things to human beings, utterly devoid of universal experience, hemmed in by their limited sensory experiences of five senses, and lacking in dimensional concepts other than space-time, what would you do? You would interpret spiritual things in terms of those five senses and four dimensions, with evident gaps. Heaven would be like a city with streets of transparent gold and certain gates of single pearls, or a fantastically commodious house combining many mansions. The fact that God is in the midst of believers gathered in His Name suggests a presence like that

93]

of a dearly beloved friend, out of sight but within conversational distance. Obviously His presence is more than that, but it is not detectable through ordinary sensory experimentation and only partly understood. How different our present interpretation of the universe would be if we had ten other senses besides the five we have, each as different as sight is from sound!

Good and evil have no absolute meaning in materialistic concepts. Bombing human life out of existence would not be wrong in any absolute sense because all life would presumably come to an end in the due course of time, anyway. Perhaps thousands, or even millions, of planets with life superior to our own would have come to a tragic close by being overheated, supercooled, or subjected to devastation by a minute cosmic ripple.

On the other hand, if God spoke to Moses on Mount Sinai and to others at significant periods of history, good and evil have absolute meaning, and redemption is essential. Science, in order to be complete, must include this true God.

One cannot help but think in this connection of Paul the Apostle, born and raised in the highly intellectual center of Tarsus and recipient of a splendid education in Jerusalem— one cannot help but think of him in advanced age writing from Laodicea to his spiritual son Timothy and admonishing him with all the fervor of his dedicated soul: "O Timothy, keep that which is committed to thy trust, avoiding profane and vain babblings, and opposition of science falsely so called!" (I Timothy 6: 20) What Paul probably had in mind, chiefly, was the philosophy and science of the Stoics, one of whose high seats of learning was in Tarsus where the apostle received his early training, and whose teachings concerning the universe were utterly materialistic. To them, matter and force were the ultimate principles in the universe. Their sages in numerous stoas taught that man should ignore and put himself above any "unrealistic" feelings such as love, sympathy, compassion.

It should not take too keen a mind to identify their counterparts in our modern world.

A YOUNG MYSTIC PROCEEDS TO CLEAR THINKING

BY RUSSELL LOWELL MIXTER

ZOOLOGIST

M.Sc., Michigan State University, Ph.D., University of Illinois; Professor of Zoology and Chairman of Science Division, Wheaton College; member of Illinois Academy of Science; president, 1951–54, of American Scientific Affiliation. Specialist in macrophages of connective tissue, spiders of Black Hills, evolution.

THE first meeting one usually has with God is through his parents. They use God's name with reverence, so a child learns by their example. In his early and small needs he will pray to God in simple fashion, just as he asks a favor of his own father. He is satisfied and continues to trust in his Unseen Parent.

Later in books he learns the stories of people who walked with God. He learns that they "stopped the mouths of lions, quenched the violence of fire, escaped the edge of the sword, out of weakness were made strong, waxed valiant in fight." How the child is thrilled with their heroism and challenged by their examples! He knows he has a help toward honesty. He feels he has companions of the past who are "a cloud of witnesses" to encourage him on his course in life.

School days both build up and crumble his faith. He learns his country is an intricate society with many groups interwoven with others, led by dominant personalities, and all supervised by a President who can make decisions and have people carry them out. To a student God is like the President, a person with much authority which he exercises over others. As it is reasonable that there should be a ruler over men, so it is also logical that there should be a superhuman Person with authority over all humanity.

On the other hand, if a ruler is set up by vote or consent of the people, it may be that God is merely an idea people have, an idea which has no real existence except in their minds. They perhaps invented their God! This thought perplexes the student. He wonders if there is a God at all. How can he be sure?

In these circumstances he may merely lay aside all intellectual difficulties and accept the existence of God as a belief, asking not to be disturbed by thinking friends. He becomes a mystic, convinced that there is a God because he so desperately wishes one, but never sure at the times when he lets his reasoning processes come into contact with his faith.

One day our young mystic pages through his Bible, and he comes across a passage which says that true religion is something "reasonable," and a footnote tells him that "reasonable" in these modern times would have been translated "rational" (Romans 12: 1). That stops him. That seems to tell him that the human *mind* has something to do with being religious, after all. A long season of study and investigation follows.

Eventually the young mystic becomes a man of faith and a Christian thinker. He *believes* and *knows* that God exists. Soul and intellect live and function in harmony. He is now ready to strive for the Scriptural ideal: "That the man of God may be perfect, thoroughly furnished unto all good works."

This writer's work keeps him in close touch with Nature and Nature's God. One cannot, in good logic, separate the two.

He encounters a huge variety of living plants and animals; also evidences that an immense number lived in the past. There are probably a million species of animals on this earth. I am talking about *species*, not individual animals, whose number of course runs into astronomical figures. Of plants one could find at least two hundred thousand species.

Order in such an array? There is order everywhere! Take just one of the one million species of animals. Each such species falls into groups, and each group can again be subdivided. But divide and subdivide as you will, the characteristics and similarities of the species will be found in all. One woodpecker, for example, has similarities that are common to all the woodpeckers. The Downy looks very much like the Hairy, but somewhat less like the Sapsucker, and so forth.

There is, then, not a completely disorganized array of forms, but a pervading similarity of greater or less degree all through Nature. If one basic material—flesh, protoplasm—can be found with infinitely varied arrangements of it in living things, and if at the same time a host of similarities can be found in a thousand-and-one different groupings, then it is certainly evident that back of it all is the thoughtful planning of a God who made the basic material and gave it the poten-

[98

tiality and directiveness of producing endless variations of itself.

Logic compels us to assume that a Divine Mind has conceived, planned and executed the variations and similarities here discussed, rather than to assume that somehow this varied living material came into being by accidental combinations of elements, or a cohesion of elements more or less channeled by environment. The same logical mind which notices that a human mind makes complicated things concludes that complicated living beings have been made by the Master Mind. No matter how much these beings vary among the members of one species, and no matter how much change there seems to have been in a species as it is traced back toward its ancestors, living and fossilized, one cannot fail to observe that it began with a well adapted creature. And a "creature" it was—the handiwork of a Creator!

When one reads in the Bible that God created man, animals, and plants, he can readily believe it, for what he has seen in Nature is in harmony with that belief. The Bible is not a textbook of science. But it does furnish the foundational principles of science. And what to me is an ever-shining, never-dimming truth—a truth that loses none of its luster in the presence of every materialistic theory ever conceived or devised—is the fact that the God of the Bible and the God of Nature are one and the same.

It is the God of the Bible who talks to me through the mountains, the skies and the seas. It is His voice that whispers sweetly through a lovely landscape, freshly green, with birds chirping and frisky animals gamboling about.

FOOTSTEPS OF GOD IN THE PLANT WORLD

BY GERALD T. DEN HARTOG

RESEARCH AGRONOMIST

M.Sc., Ph.D., University of Minnesota; Research Agronomist, Cotton and Other Fibers Branch, Agricultural Research Service, U.S. Department of Agriculture; member American Society of Agronomists. Specialist in cotton breeding, field crop pathology, quantitative inheritance, biostatistics.

THIS present chapter will deal chiefly with plant breeding and genetics (heredity, etc.). The first recorded allusion to some type of inheritance in plants is found in the first chapter of Genesis: "And God said, Let the earth bring forth grass, the herb yielding seed, and the fruit tree yielding fruit after his kind, whose seed is in itself upon the earth. And it was so. And the earth brought forth grass, and herb yielding seed after his kind, and the tree yielding fruit, whose seed was in itself, after his kind. And God saw that it was good."

Only by delving into our subject somewhat thoroughly can we establish the *scientific* authenticity of the Genesis report, aside from our spiritual faith in the Bible record.

[100

The rediscovery of Mendel's laws in 1900 by de Vries, Correns and von Tschermak, each working independently, ushered in the science of modern genetics. Based on results of numerous experiments conducted in the 1850's and 1860's, G. J. Mendel formulated the fundamental laws of segregation and independent assortment. These laws, together with the discovery of linkage by W. Bateson and R. C. Punnett in 1906, and the establishment of the chromosome as the seat of heredity by T. H. Morgan in 1919, form the foundation of modern genetics.

In actual practice, plant inheritance is much more complex than the one- or two-factor cases studied by Mendel. The basic principles, however, still apply. Many of the important agronomic characters (traits, or characteristics) of crop plants are multiple-factor in nature (subject to various influences). Also, there is only partial dominance, or incomplete dominance, of the individual factors. In addition, the expression of many characters is influenced considerably by environment.

The virescent (turning green) characters in maize (corn) are an example. In the seedling stage and under low temperature conditions the leaves are yellow. As the plant advances in age the leaves turn green and assume a normal appearance. Under other environmental conditions, such as warmer temperatures, certain of the virescent characters may not even be discernible.

The plant expression which we see is called the phenotype, a term indicating the sum total of visible traits which characterize the members of a group. This phenotype is made up of three components: that due to genotype (genetic), that due to environment, and that due to the interaction between genotype and environment. Only the genetic component of a plant's expression is inherited and constant.

For example, if a barley variety is grown in Minnesota in the first year without selection, and in the cool environment of Alaska the second season, and back to Minnesota the third season, and compared with unselected progenies grown in Minnesota all three years, there is no evidence that the slightest change has occurred in the variety. In other words, the genetic potential of the phenotype was unaltered by growing the plants in widely different environments.

The phenotype of plants is affected not only by the physical environment but also by its biological environment. In the growing of oats in the United States, the expression is often used among agriculturists that the oats have "run out" when referring to the fact that a particular "rust resistant" oats variety may after several years begin to exhibit susceptibility to stem or crown rust. Growers often mistakenly attribute this "running out" or deterioration to a change in the variety. Actually, the development of disease susceptibility may have been due to a linkage between factors for resistance to the known physiologic race (breed) of rust and factors for susceptibility to some unknown new race. Also, oat rusts have the ability to hybridize in the presence of the alternate hosts "Berberis vulgaris" (in the case of stem rust) and "Rhamnus catharticus" (in the case of crown rust), and thus produce new physiologic races.

The pattern of disease resistance in higher plants is an intricate one, resulting from the interaction of two complex biological systems, the host and the pathogen (an agent capable of producing disease). In the example of oats, the *apparent* change in variety was the result of a change in the local population of pathogenic (disease producing) organisms attacking the plant, rather than any genetic change in the variety itself.

A plant species has been defined by the French botanist de Jussieu as "the perennial succession of similar individuals perpetuated by generation." The members of a species have definite stem, leaf, and flower characteristics that are distinguishable over and above the thousands of recognizable genetic variants which may occur within the species. By natural selection and human selection progress has been made in obtaining biotypes within each of the domesticated species that are more productive and better adapted than the prevalent types of several hundred years ago. There is reason to believe that this progress will continue in the future. However—and this is the great point to be stressed—basically the plant species remain the same all through the ages, regardless of selective processes, changes in climate and environment, or persistent and widespread attacks by biological enemies. The Creator's mandate in Genesis I is being carried out to this very day.

A striking illustration of the persistency of plant species is provided by the archaeological finds of wheat seed and other plant products that correspond to our present-day species and that have remained relatively unchanged over thousands of years. In his book on the history of cotton G. Watt reports that Theophrastus in 350 B.C. described "wool bearing" trees growing in what is now Bahrein, on the Persian Gulf. Tree cottons, known as "gossypium arboreum," are very much in existence today.

It is true, mutations (alterations) occur in plant life, though with extreme infrequency—chromosomal mutations

103]

and gene mutations. But also these leave the species itself intact. Chromosomal mutations involve the loss of an entire chromosome or the deletion, inversion, or translocation of a chromosome segment. Gene mutations also occur. Such mutations, involving a single locus, have been studied on a large number of organisms. By the use of X-rays and mutator genes Muller studied the equivalent of some 1,000 or more generations of the fruit fly, *Drosophila melanogaster,* and reports that the mutated genes are all deleterious or at best similar in effect to the original gene complex. Stadler obtained similar results from his X-ray studies of barley seeds. All these and similar studies indicated that there was no change in the species.

In the absence of selection and mutation cross-fertilization may be attempted, but Hardy's formula (an intricate formula well known among modern agronomists) shows that eventually genetic equilibrium is reached. The mechanism of heredity always tends to stabilize the species and to keep it within the bounds of its original type.

This writer believes that there is a God who reveals himself constantly through the unfailing laws, the mysteries and wonders of the plant world. He reveals himself in the following ways:

1. Orderliness.   The processes of plant growth and reproduction as brought about by cell enlargement, division, and specialization of function proceed in a systematic, regular, and marvelously undeviating manner.

2. Complexity.   No man-made machine today equals the complexity of operations involved in the growth and reproduction of a single, simple plant.

3. Beauty.   The Divinely artistic beauty of plants—stems,

leaves and flowers—greatly exceeds that which the greatest genius among men has produced.

4. Inheritance.   Plants reproduce after their kind, unfailingly. Inheritance does not proceed in a wild, haphazard, uncontrolled manner. Wheat produces wheat, barley barley, an olive tree an olive tree, under all sorts of environment, generation after generation.

To me, all this indicates the existence of a Creator-God, limitless both in knowledge and in power.

FACTS FROM A FORESTER'S FIELDBOOK

BY LAURENCE COLTON WALKER

RESEARCH FORESTER AND PLANT PHYSIOLOGIST

B.Sc., Pennsylvania State University, M.For., Yale University, Ph.D., State University of New York College of Forestry at Syracuse University; formerly Research Forester, U.S. Forest Service; presently Associate Professor of silviculture in charge of the forest physiology laboratory, University of Georgia School of Forestry. Specialist in forest soils, plant physiology, silvicides for hardwood control, radioisotopology.

"God is not the author of confusion." (Bible) Quite in contrast, His creative acts are systematically arranged to exhibit order at its highest level.

Often the layman merely views the summits from the valley and then ascribes the nobleness of the hills to God; or hears repeated "Solomon in all his glory was not arrayed like one of these" in the rustle of wind breaking the silence of the lily-studded field.

True, this grandeur is the handiwork of the Master Architect. But to seek no further for evidences of personal providential creative activities is not unlike one's admiration for a carpenter's handsome home—admiration for the manner in which the siding is tacked to the frame, but never troubling to note the exactness with which the joists are leveled, the corners squared, or the interior ornaments tooled by hand.

If God's government of the universe were limited to the creation of fertile valley fields from the alluvial sediments of eroding hills, His energies would not be highly regarded by the forest physiographer or physiologist. To see His designs and purpose one needs to focus sharply, with aperture wide, upon the minutiae of field and forest. Then the natural becomes the supernatural; and to believe in the supernatural is to believe in God at work.

Karl Heim in his recent volume *Christian Faith and Natural Science* phrased it thus:

> The marvellous constitution of the world's structure not only *permits* the influence of an intellectual Creator, but *invites* such an inference. The line of approach from Nature to God which was pursued by men of the Enlightenment and Rationalism, but which was blocked in the age of causal-mechanism, is now open again following the breakdown of the causal-mechanism world-view.

From my own experiences as a research forester dealing primarily with ecology (mutual relations between trees and their environment) and tree physiology, I pen these few notes of the witness of the woods:

Re-creating forest soils. In the Adirondack Mountains deep sands of glacial outwash origin occur. Under native vegetation the acid soils develop weak to medium podzolic characteristics. Basic nutrients, particularly potassium, except for the portion retained by the organic component, are leached from the soil as rapidly as released by mineral decomposition. These "sand plains" once supported forests of spruce, pine and hemlock, but the favorable topography led to cultivation early in the nineteenth century. A hundred years of intensive farming resulted in depletion of natural fertility. Finally the plains were abandoned and reforestation by planting took place.

A few years after planting of spruces, and white and red pines, symptoms of potassium deficiency in the soil occurred. Further investigation showed that certain native weed trees, such as gray birch and wild black cherry, produced foliage symptoms of potassium shortage and that these abnormal colorations could be used as guides for prospective planting sites. God's creative (and I use the term in the present, active sense) orderliness in rebuilding man's mess was most apparent. Not only did He provide guides for where not to plant the spruces and red and white pines, but other species of commercial value, like scotch and jack pines, exist which do not suffer from low levels of soil-potassium. It was also found that foliage of *Andropogon* grass, wild strawberry, several weed trees, and even white pine could be quantitatively analyzed to determine site potential. White pine, for instance, always exhibits deficiency symptoms when less than 0.5% K (potassium) is in the needles. This foliar K is correlated to 20 ppm of exchangeable K in the soil.

Still another phenomenon was observed. White birch, ordinarily a weed species, seeds-in abundantly and thrives hardily in the plains. But under the crowns of these "nurse" trees white pines also seed-in and dense seedling and sapling stands result. The pines are found on all sides of the birches, but only to the crown edge. None of the characteristics of potassium deficiency are manifested by these overtopped trees. Soil and foliage analyses showed that exchangeable potassium was over three times as great under the birch-pine groups as in the open, and the differences in the amount of the element in the foliage were statistically highly significant for the two conditions. Thus, the "foraging" capacity of white birch is providing a way for restoring nutrients to agriculturally-depleted soils; and mineral nutrition is the Master Workman's bridge between "dead" inorganic material and the world of life.

A similar vegetation influence was noted in the Connecticut Valley where eastern redcedar, accompanied by the lowly earthworm, was responsible for greatly increasing calcium levels. Redcedar leaves deposit calcium on the forest floor, although tied up organically. Attracted by the high lime content of the foliage, earthworms rapidly digest the foliage and, in doing so, release calcium as a readily available nutrient for plant growth.

In the redcedar case, not only was nutrition effected, but all the physical characteristics of a soil which are instrumental in flood control—porosity, infiltration rate, field capacity, and volume height—were significantly improved.

But more may be said for the Divine plan of restoring lost soils. (Is there a human analogy here?) Under virgin conditions forests are perpetuated, and the climax type, like the oak-hickory of the Southland and the beech-birch-maple of the Alleghenies, predominates and reproduces itself *ad infinitum* unless disturbed by man, fire, or storm. It is man's influence, in cropping or grazing lands best suited for timber, which destroys trees and soil. Floods follow.

Man makes costly efforts to reduce the damage of the

floods by large dam-construction projects. But these are only temporary injunctions against a power no rock and concrete wall can contain. True flood prevention must tackle the problem at its source. It is not in building dams but in restoring vegetation to the land. Such land restoration is freely given. Within a year after eroded old-fields have been abandoned, dense grasses, herbs, shrubs and tree seedlings have invaded and begun their work of rehabilitation. Often in the lower Piedmont Province of the Eastern United States twenty-five years will see the establishment of a new and distinct humus horizon at the surface of the soil. Even in colder climates, where organic decay progresses more slowly, restored A horizons are not uncommonly seen within fifty years following abandonment. While the soil is never again equal to the virgin state for flood prevention purposes, its redemption is a worthy cause.

Goethe puts it this way:

> There is no trifling with Nature. It is always true, grave, and severe. It is always in the right, and the faults and errors fall to our share. It defies incompetency, but reveals its secrets to the competent, the truthful, and the pure.

Recreating forest stands. When *Endothia*, the pathogen responsible for chestnut blight, spread rapidly in the first two decades of the century, many visualized holes in the forest canopy which would never be filled. The unique position which the American chestnut occupied was unsurpassed by any other species. High-grade, rot-resistant lumber, wood pulp, tannin, nuts, and shade were a few of its uses; and it grew on poor mountain ridges, as well as in rich fertile valleys. Until *Endothia* arrived from Asia about 1900, nothing attacked the chestnut. It was truly king of the forest. Now,

[110

it is practically extinct as a forest tree. Only sprouts from stumps of once-lofty stems remain as grim reminders that the mightiest—men as well as trees—may fall.

But the holes in the forest stand were filled. Tuliptrees were waiting for just such openings in the canopy which would provide sufficient light for that shade-intolerant species to develop. Until then these trees were minor components of the forest, only occasionally developing into valuable timber trees. Now, however, chestnut trees are hardly missed where dense stands of tuliptrees have become established, often growing as much as one inch in diameter and six feet in height per year. In addition to fast growth, wood of superior quality, especially for rotary-cut veneer purposes, is produced. Is the master plan of Nature executed by more than a set of circumstances?

On the subject of how to manage chestnut-blighted areas an old-time National Forest ranger, with whom I delight to observe Nature, is continually admonishing others, in their silvicultural decisions, to open Nature's book and find the answer. Isaac Watts phrased it rhythmically:

> Nature with open volume stands
> To spread her Maker's praise abroad.

The eminent botanist, Asa Gray, in his Yale lectures of 1880, so indicated, saying, "No Christian theist can . . . agree that what science removes from the supernatural to the natural is lost to theism. But the business of science is with the course of Nature, not with interruptions of it . . . it is the business and privilege of science . . . to refer events and phenomena not at the first but in the last resort to Divine will."

New light on an original creation. Plants contain hormones which function in various ways. A single such compound, 2-4-5-T, serves to ripen tomatoes, inhibits sprouting of stored potatoes, actuates rooting of vegetative cuttings, and perhaps a host of other metabolic functions yet to be discovered. This hormone, or more properly *growth regulator,* since it is a synthetic organic compound which behaves like a hormone, is currently under scrutiny in our laboratory. The fact that the Master Synthesizer constructed molecules which could be very closely simulated by man is evidence of an orderly creation.

We are particularly interested in the behavior of the radioactive equivalent of this compound in forest trees. The last carbon (C^{12}) shown in the chain is synthetically exchanged with its isotope (C^{14}), a weak beta emitter. With C^{14} as a tagged tracer, the route and rate of movement is readily followed—from leaves to stem to root. To an agnostic this may be sheer magic, but to us it is a revelation of the directive power of God.

Of great importance in these studies is the fact that the compound remains as 2-4-5-T, regardless of its apparent destiny in the tree. Less than 10 percent is converted to other compounds by chemical exchange. Of equal importance is the fact that regardless of the dose applied to leaf surfaces, only a minute amount is absorbed. The plant apparently permits only a bare excess for its purposes to be absorbed in the metabolic stream. The host of questions which this technique presents is evidence to those who seek their answers in the vast unexplored depths of the cosmos—the ordered Whole of Nature—of a Supreme Intelligent Author.

We test for 2-4-5-T by the paper chromatographic (composite color tones) technique. The method involves spotting a drop of the unknown near the end of a strip of filter paper. That end is then placed in a dish of "developer," with the other end hanging over the dish. By capillarity (mutual attraction of molecules—minute particles of matter) the developer is absorbed, carrying with it the components of the drop. Each organic component will be deposited on the chromatographic map at a particular spot, as the capillary stream progresses, and no other compound will be found there. Done! The picture is complete! A geiger counter passed over the paper reveals the location of the C^{14}.

Here is evidence that Nature is an ordered and fixed system of forms, what Hägelis called its "principle of perfection." Here, in the organic molecule, the C^{14} atom, and finally in the electron ejected from the atom on the paper, is an example to the earnest inquirer of the revelation that there can be no real conflict between science and God. God reveals Himself to man through science; through such mighty works as those here described. As the great apostle-philosopher Paul phrased it: "He (God revealed in Christ) is before all things, and by Him all things consist." And as Philips in his *Letters to Young Churches* translates Paul elsewhere, freely, and in the modern vernacular: "Indeed He has made the truth quite plain. For since the beginning of the world the invisible attributes of God, e.g., His eternal power and divinity, have been plainly discernible through the things which He has made and which are commonly seen and known." (Col. I: 17; Rom. I: 19, 20)

THINGS A FRUIT RANCHER'S BOY LEARNED

BY WALTER EDWARD LAMMERTS

GENETICIST

B.Sc., Ph.D., University of California. Formerly Director of Research, Armstrong Nurseries, Ontario, Calif.; Professor of Ornamental Horticulture, University of California, Los Angeles; Director of Research, Descanso Gardens, La Canada, Calif.; since 1954 in charge of rose research, Descanso Distributors, Germain's and Amling-De Vor Nurseries, Livermore, Calif. Specialist in the breeding of ornamental plants, especially roses.

PROBABLY a truthful answer to the question "Why do I believe in God?" would be, "Because my parents taught me to." That is the usual way the Divine Spirit works. But they also taught me to believe in Santa Claus and Easter Bunnies. Though I soon saw through these delightful childhood fairy tales, I grew more impressed as the years went by with the creative wisdom and power of God.

As a fruit rancher's boy the behavior of the various apples, peaches and pears, and their remarkable though only partial adaptation to the 20° below zero eastern Washington area of Kennewick, fascinated me. Their wondrously beautiful burst of flowers each spring, after looking so dead all winter, always thrilled me deeply. But since they were not completely adapted to our climate, late frosts often killed all the blossoms and there was no crop, and everyone in the little valley suffered hardship.

My first and frequent thoughts were along the line of—Why, if God is good, does He permit such frequent crop losses? Soon the answer was clear: it was not God's fault but man's. We were trying to grow varieties not fully adapted to our Kennewick climate. In their localities of origin they flowered later in the season, after the danger of frost was over. Hence, though all were designed for temperate zones, each variety was remarkably precise in its adaptation and only by careful breeding and selection could they be adapted to varying climates.

Evidently then all plants and animals were not only created for their original environment but also with a variable amount of genetic variability potential, allowing them to become adapted to other climates in case the necessity should arise. The study of this remarkable ability of plants and animals to vary is called genetics, and because of my boyhood experiments in growing and studying the variations in peach seedlings, I was keen to learn as much about it as possible.

In addition to growing seedlings of peach trees and flowers I was much interested in the various insects, particularly those responsible for cross pollination such as the bees and their mimics, the bee-flies (*Bomby liidae*). How could this remarkable parallel variation have come about? The fascinating books of Jean Henri Fabre on the wonders of insect instincts and their intricate patterns of social life gave further evidence of a most amazing design in Nature.

All through this it was equally obvious that some contrary force was at work, perverting, or at least distorting, the use of plants and animals by man, in such a way that often there were too many ants and not enough bees, either no fruit or so much that we could not sell it, and soil which though decreasing in fertility yet yielded increasingly luxuriant crops of weeds. Just why should this be? Nature did not give the answer, but the Bible did. A Divine curse lay upon the soil and Nature generally since the fall of man. Nevertheless, enough remains of the original goodness of creation to show clearly the amazing power and wisdom of God, and it is our task, to the extent of our capabilities, to help restore the earth to its former state of beauty and perfection.

Such then was my philosophy when I started college and came in contact with the materialistic evolution theory, the only philosophy which seriously questions or indeed attempts to replace belief in design in Nature as proof of God's creative power. A number of years of intense mental struggle resulted, both within myself and with some of the older graduate students. Several facts became clear. For instance, the science of genetics offered no evidence for belief in the two most basic assumptions of Charles Darwin (*Origin of Species*)—(1) that young organisms of each generation continuously tend to vary slightly from their parents in all possible directions, and (2) that favorable changes are inherited by the next generation and accentuated until extensive changes are built up.

In fact, as discussed in considerable detail by W. J. Tinkle and myself in our book *Modern Science and Christian*

Faith, the end point of variability in any plant or animal is soon reached by selective breeding. Self-pollination in plants or inbreeding in animals results in far less vigorous lines. Except for occasional mutations (changes), such lines breed true and do not continue to vary in all possible directions as postulated by Darwin. The occurrence of occasional mutations in them is, however, eagerly pointed to by evolutionists as the material basis of evolution. But are they really? Long continued study of them in many organisms, but especially in the fruit fly, *Drosophila melanogaster,* indicates that most mutations are lethal. Among the non-lethal ones the majority are defective changes, or at least neutral ones, which have associated physiological effects that decrease the general ruggedness of the individual. Therefore, an accumulation of such heritable mutations would hardly give us the sort of changes needed for species formation.

On rare occasions a mutation such as that of the fruit fly wing called "eversae" does show more viability (capacity to live) —104% at 75–77°F.—but combination of it with others affecting the wing structure results in flies of markedly decreased viability. But even supposing mutations conferring a 1% advantage do rarely occur, just how rapidly can they be accumulated in a species? Patau (Mathematical Analysis of the Evolution Theory) has shown that it would take about 1,000,000 generations to effect a population breeding true for this new mutation. Certainly, even granting the immense periods of time postulated by geologists, it is difficult to see how such a relatively modern animal as the horse would have evolved from its presumed five-toed doglike ancestor since the relatively recent Eocene times.

Finally, study of the remarkably intricate structures called chromosomes, in which the factors determining the characteristics of the body are located, shows remarkable variation in their make-up and pattern, even in such closely related species as *Drosophila melanogaster* and *Drosophila pseudoobscura* (fruit flies). In fact, in his *Genetics and the Origin of Species* Dobzhansky says: "Some chromosome sections have been so thoroughly rebuilt by repeated inversions and translocations that their disc patterns in the salivary chromosomes no longer resemble each other." And yet all studies so far of either artificially induced or naturally occurring translocations in the fruit fly show that practically all of them are incapable of living when homozygous (of the same essential characters and features)! How then could these striking differences in chromosome arrangement have come about?

Many more facts could be presented were space not limited showing that the materialistic evolution theory simply cannot account for the variations we see in the animate world. They clearly point to a remarkably wise Creator who made living creatures capable of a limited amount of variation, so as to be able to survive even in the ever changing conditions of a world more adverse than that in which they originally were created.

However, a study of Nature can only show the power and wisdom of its Creator and not His ultimate purpose. As Paul the Apostle so aptly says: "For now we see through a glass darkly, but then face to face; now I know in part, but then shall I know even as also I am known."

TRILLIONS OF LIVING CELLS
SPEAK THEIR MESSAGE

BY RUSSELL CHARLES ARTIST

BIOLOGIST AND BOTANIST

B.Sc., Butler University, M.Sc., Northwestern University, Ph.D., University of Minnesota. Graduate study at University of Zürich, Switzerland. Professor at Frankfurt-on-the-Main, Germany, College for several years; since 1953 Professor and Head of Department of Biology at David Lipscomb College, Nashville, Tenn. Member of Academies of Science of Indiana, Tennessee, and Texas. Author of several biological monographs.

To observe living cells is an amazing experience. Mount the tip of a leaf of the little water weed *Elodea* under the microscope and bring it under the high power objective. A most beautiful and well-ordered manifestation of life appears. Each of the cells shows a magnificent structure. The leaf at the tip of the plant generally has a thickness of two layers of cells, but by focusing sharply the outlines of individual cells can be seen in optical section. Each cell seems to be a unit in itself, each apparently capable of carrying on its life activities independently of others like itself. The walls of

119]

the cells, separating one cell from another, are rigid and unchanging. The entire leaf is made up of many hundreds of such cells, overlapping each other like the bricks in a masonry wall.

Often the nucleus can be faintly seen, a dull grey body bulging out into the central vacuole of cavity of the cell but held within a thin ribbon of cytoplasm extending around the innermost edge. Next to the cell, we know, a thin and very delicate membrane exists. It cannot under ordinary circumstances be seen for it is pressed very tightly againt the wall by the pressure of the water or cell sap within the cell. When the slide is flooded with strong salt water, however, the membrane becomes clearly visible, for as the water is drawn outward the contents of the cell shrink within the membrane. We then say the cell has been plasmolyzed.

But there is movement here, too! And movement such as one would hardly believe to exist in a plant leaf seemingly so rigid from the outside. Around the very innermost edge of the cell, in the thin cytoplasmic film, are minute green bodies called chloroplasts. They are not actively propelling themselves like some microscopic animals but are floating along like tiny boats in a stream. It is this watery protoplasm which is itself alive and moving. Here, then, is truly the physical basis of life in motion. In this particular plant the moving of the chloroplasts seems to be a manifestation, a visible means of detection, of one of the general characteristics by which we recognize life—movement!

The force or forces which are at work to cause this moving stream of protoplasm we do not know certainly, nor can we in the present state of our knowledge even attempt to explain the phenomenon adequately. But it is seen here and there in the world of living things, both in plant cells and in animal cells. This phenomenon is called protoplasmic streaming or, by some, cyclosis, especially in *Elodea* where a cyclic streaming of the living protoplasm is made visible to our eyes by the motion of the green plastids in moving around and around just inside the wall of the cell.

Now place a drop of the protozoan culture containing the organism Amoeba on a warmed microscope slide and the same amazing streaming of the protoplasm may be seen. The animal does not swim; neither does it passively float in or on the drop of water—it actually and literally flows! Unlike the plant cells this bit of naked protoplasm which is the animal itself has no rigid wall but only a thin limiting membrane, so that as it flows it changes shape and develops extensions of the body. Because of some fancied resemblance to a foot, these extensions of the body—first thrust out in this direction and then in another—have been called pseudopodia or false feet.

Under high magnification actual particles of matter can be seen flowing out into the false feet as the animal moves along. Two regions of different density of protoplasm can be recognized: an inner more hyaline or watery mass almost constantly in a state of motion and an outer, semi-solid or jellylike, mass completely encasing the former. Some scientists believe that these two densities help to provide for the movement, the outer plasmagel squeezing in upon the watery plasmasol causing it to flow out into the pseudopodia (false feet). Others believe that it is merely due to surface tension.

This is a common phenomenon witnessed by students every year in beginning biology courses, yet we cannot tell them why it occurs. Even if we should accept the former theory

121]

as to the nature and cause of amoeboid movement (the solation and gelation of the protoplasm) we still must admit that
we know virtually nothing about the metabolic processes of
the cell which would cause it.

Here, then, are two widely different kinds of cells; one
from a green plant, the other an individual animal organism.
Each is, in many respects, a simple cell or unit. The amoeba
has been called by many zoologists the most primitive of all
animals, and, indeed, the streaming of its protoplasm is the
simplest of all the means of locomotion in the animal world.
Elodea, though a small flowering plant, has cells that are not
markedly differentiated as in many other plants. Surely we
can say they are simple cells. Yet each is a highly organized
system, performing the necessary and intricate functions of
life in its own way and at the same time making visible to our
senses by the streaming of the protoplasm one of the com-
monest attributes of life. Each cell performs these activities
with a precision that by comparison makes the running of
even the finest watch a clumsy affair.

Speaking of watches, to be sure, there are many fine
watches made, some even with self-winding devices, which,
when once started, keep the time-piece running by the movement of one's arm. Now, it cannot be demonstrated successfully that such a precision instrument as a watch came to
exist by accident, that is, without the mind and hand of the
craftsman, nor that, even in the self-winding type, it began
without someone setting it in motion. When we ask concerning the living cell: "How did this microscopic but amazing
functional unit come to have its present form?" or "How was
it set in motion?" we are confronted with formidable, even
insuperable, difficulties in trying to account for its beginning

and, for that matter, its continued functioning, unless we maintain with reason and logic that an intelligence, a mind, brought it into existence. This Mind, this Supreme Intelligence, as contrasted with unthinking Matter, is God.

It must be admitted that there are, to be sure, external and a-biotic forces in the environment which seem to affect the streaming of protoplasm in cells. Certain researchers report that a variety of stimuli, such as temperature, perhaps light, or osmotic pressure (pressure due to differences of concentration) influence the solation and gelation of the living substance, but they are as quick to assert that streaming, especially cyclosis (circular motion), goes on continuously in many cells in the absence of any apparent external stimulation. Therefore, it seems to be at least in part under the control of the protoplasm itself. There appears to be more to this cell than just the response to outside stimuli.

In this connection we also know that an enucleated cell, in which the nucleus has been removed by microdissection, soon dies; all attempts to maintain it end in failure. The organizer of the cell is gone—the cell cannot continue to live. Just so the Organizer of the universe is necessary to the creation of a cell—and to the minds of reasoning men searching for a first cause.

Not just because I do not at present know or understand this phenomenon of protoplasmic action of the cells am I driven to the conclusion that God exists. Certainly, many use the argument that because science does not know, therefore we must accept God. I am *not* using this argument. Even if we were some day to unveil the present mystery of this streaming matter and come to understand the living cell more perfectly, we should only be following with our own intellect

123]

a greater Mind that set it in motion in the beginning and kept it operating.

Many theories have been brought forward in the attempt to derive living cells from inanimate matter. Certain investigators are claiming that life has originated through the protogene, or through viruses, or through an aggregation of large protein molecules, which may leave the impression that at last the gap between the lifeless and the living has been spanned. Actually it must be admitted that all attempts to produce living matter experimentally from inanimate matter have failed utterly.

Furthermore, it is not by direct evidence that the one who denies the existence of God proves to a waiting world that a fortuitous aggregation of atoms and molecules is life, capable of maintaining and directing itself as do the cells described here. Not at all. He accepts this as a *belief*. It is his private interpretation of the facts visible to us all, that an accidental concourse brought the first cell into being. But this is to accept an even greater miracle than to believe that Intelligence called it into being!

I maintain that each of these single cells (each a system so intricate and delicate that its complete functioning has so far escaped our study), and all the trillions of them on this earth, definitely present a justifiable inference—one of Mind, or Intelligence, or Thought, which we call God. Science both admits and accepts this inference.

I believe firmly that there is a God.

THE REASONABLENESS OF THEISM

BY GEORGE HERBERT BLOUNT

APPLIED PHYSICIST

B.A., University of California at Los Angeles, M.Sc., California Institute of Technology. Formerly Staff Member of the Los Alamos Physics Group; Chief Instrument Engineer of the Aerodynamic Test Division of the University of Southern California's Engineering Center; now Head of the Analysis Group of the Point Mugu Bendix Aviation Facility.

I BELIEVE in God. Far more than this, I trust in God. For to me the concept of deity is not only a philosophical cornerstone—it is a dominant practical consideration. God is a part of my daily endeavor.

This is in sharp contrast to the view of many first-rate thinkers. Not a few intellectual giants have driven God from their world. And since the faith of atheism is not without its preachers, God's exit has had wide acclaim. There is, therefore, an obligation to present the reasoning behind the theistic position.

As an attempt to help execute this obligation, I wish to indicate some of my own reflections. First, I wish to consider some of the major evidences for and against theism. A consideration of these things provides an understanding of why a

125]

reasonable man can, and should, believe in God. Then, I wish to suggest why a man *does* believe in God.

Those evidences of God which are in no way connected with individual enlightenment have been subject to much study and analysis. The discussion of the ages has expanded the implications of the universal evidences to the lofty heights of the Christian concept and, then, in another breath, shrivelled them to a Spencer's "Unknowable." Such discord of deductive dogma appears to be the norm.

Upon the testimony of the bulk of philosophical thought, the universal evidences lead to what might be called a God, but not of necessity to the God of, say, the Bible. This weakness of the evidences in the interpretive hands of philosophy does not, of course, rule out the possibility of the Biblical Deity. Nor does it affirm that the vague image is completely due to a lack in the evidences: perhaps the telescope is capable of a finer adjustment than is often obtained. But, apparently, the evidences do not provide an absolute proof.

To indicate something of the true value of the evidences and what appears to me as their proper application, I would like to call to mind a parallel situation found in mathematics.

In geometry it is especially apparent that an extensive science can be built by starting with but a few axioms. The axioms are accepted without proof of their validity. The dependent science manipulates the axioms to make explicit their implications. In proving any theorem the case ultimately rests upon the axioms. However, no combination of theorems constitutes a *proof* of the axioms. To assess the value of the axioms, tests of inconsistency and physical correlation can be applied. But finding each of the theorems to be of valid practical application and finding no theorem which indicates

[126

inconsistency is, yet, less than a proof of the axioms. The axioms are still accepted on faith, though indeed not on *blind faith*.

In a similar manner, from a philosophical viewpoint, God's existence is taken axiomatically. The universal evidences are related to the demonstrations of geometry. They do not prove the basic axioms, but rather, follow from them. If a correlation exists between a demonstration and reality as we know it, then there is a bit of evidence as to the validity of the chosen axioms. The evidences consist of the correlation between what is logically expected if the theistic axioms are true and what is experimentally found true. The evidences do not destroy the element of faith, but they provide for the acceptance of the axioms on an enlightened rather than a blind basis.

The evidences have been grouped into several general categories. Examples of these are (1) the cosmological, (2) the teleological, and (3) the anthropological evidences.

The cosmological argument looks at a changing and, hence, apparently non-eternal universe, and thereby is led to a higher eternal reality. The teleological approach sees design in the universe, and therefore is forced to consider a designer. The anthropological evidences are found in the moral nature of man. Practical moral obligation is considered as an approximate interpretation of an absolute norm. The higher law demands a higher law giver.

My own scientific work is in physical analysis. Therefore, the theistic evidences which I see most often are teleological. Indeed, to determine the "laws" which govern a complex of phenomena one must first believe that order of some sort exists. It is the work of the analyst to discover the order.

The analyst begins the solution of a problem by seeking a *model* of the phenomenon. The model is a mathematical or physical approximation to the actual situation. The model is at first the supposition of the physicist. It is selected to be as simple as possible and still satisfactorily to approximate reality. The model is then investigated to determine the laws governing the situation. If comprehensive real data can be obtained and correlated with the laws derived from the model, then the model is considered to be well chosen.

It is significant that it appears that for any physical problem a model eventually can be found. It therefore seems that some kind of order is a part of reality. (How order and reality are described is a function of the prevailing mental climate.) To propose that order has arisen spontaneously from nothing, or from perhaps chaos, is somewhat uncomplimentary to a man's reason. And thus, a man, a thinking man, is led to postulate a planner of the universe he sees. Deity becomes a vital part of his set of axioms of life. God is taken into the model of reality. Correlation between the conclusion and experience is an evidence (but not a proof) of the physical validity of the axiom. If the model which includes the engineering God is true, then order should be a part of reality. Order in experience indicates that the model is valid to the limit of present experience.

Every atheist believes that he is also reasonable. And perhaps rationality should not be denied the atheist, for it has been stressed that the evidences of Deity are not proofs but rather significant indicators.

One of the more prominent features of the atheistic evidences is that they are negative. Lack of positive proof of Deity is taken to mean that Deity is not necessary. The
[128

evidences for Deity are considered not sufficient. For example, the cosmological argument is countered with the possibility that matter and energy are in unending exchange, and that therefore reality, as we know it, has had no beginning. The orderliness of Nature is considered not so orderly after all, and apparent order is considered as high quality mental fiction. Little evidence is seen for a standard of justice, and all aspects of Nature are considered *amoral*. Thus, the evidence which the atheist sees is simply that the theistic evidences are not compelling enough.

The very apparent weakness of the negative approach and, on the other hand, the lack of an absolute philosophical proof of Deity has led some to a middle position. However, it is clear that in a practical sense the atheist and the agnostic are of the same camp. Both claim that in the universe of their acquaintance there is no God. The agnostic adds little to the view of the atheist by considering it academically possible that another "universe" exists in which there may be a God. This logical mechanism is a means of averting a collision with the real question. What is meant by the question of Deity is actually: "Is there a God whose sphere of influence penetrates or encompasses at least some portion of our own sphere of activity?" Thus, one who has come to a settled agnostic view is just as much an atheist in a practical sense— the sense of ultimate importance—as the declared atheist. A man seeking his way may be in an undecided flux, but for the man who has reached his conclusion there is no practical middle ground.

By comparing the evidences for and against Deity it is clear that while neither side is provided absolute proof, the atheistic view requires considerably more faith than the theistic view. Or, more accurately stated, the faith of the theist is enlightened, but the faith of the atheist is quite blind. I am convinced that reason is the friend of theism. Of course, when one extrapolates beyond the basic evidences he is open to all sorts of uncertainties. I am not trying to justify the extensive labyrinth of good and bad produced by philosophers. But the primitive concepts of theism are reasonable. If one has failed to see the evidences, it may be because he has failed to look.

Conviction of the reasonableness of theism and the tenuousness of atheism usually in itself does not cause a man to accept practical theism. There seems to be an almost innate suspicion that the recognition of Deity will somehow rob one of freedom. To the scholar, who cherishes intellectual liberty, any thought of abridged freedom is especially dreadful. And the fear of losing freedom is not baseless. Religion for the most part has been, and is, a strait-jacket to reason. Even great branches of Christianity practice intellectual dictatorship. However, this character of religion is, obviously, a reflection of man. Philosophical tyranny is not a necessary adjunct to a deity concept. For example, the God of the Christians is portrayed in their handbook, the Bible, as bringing new and greater freedom. The Biblical injunction is, "Come now, and let us reason together, saith the Lord."

But what is it that actually causes a man to accept practical theism? I think it is not too different from that which causes a man to accept a friend's existence. A man will believe in God when he meets God.

I believe I have so encountered God—and still do. I am

glad that the theistic model of reality is reasonable, but the extent of this reasonableness and the force of its compulsion to believe is secondary: I have met God. This, of course, is a very personal experience and I do not offer it to you, if you are undecided, as a proof; you must meet God for yourself.

GEOLOGICAL DIRECTIVES

BY DONALD ROBERT CARR

GEOCHEMIST

B.Sc., University of Rochester, M.A., Ph.D., Columbia University. Formerly Research Assistant and Research Associate in Geochemistry, Columbia University; Associate Professor of Geology, Shelton College; Consultant Stanford Research Institute. Director and Vice President, since 1955, of Isotopes, Inc., New Jersey. Joint author with J. L. Kulp of "Dating with Natural Radioactive Carbon," "Use of A-57 to Determine Argon Behavior in Vacuum Systems," "The Potassium-Argon Method of Geochronometry," and other publications. Specialist in geological age determination, using methods based on natural radioactivity; nuclear processes in atmospheric and geologic setting.

IT is impossible for me to enter a discussion of the existence of God with an open mind. This may sound rather unscientific. But let me explain—and thereafter make a few remarks of a purely scientific nature.

When we are called upon to give a reason for our beliefs we can from scientific studies marshal evidence which allows us to establish the high probability of the existence of God —though not necessarily the God of the Bible. We can go

[132

beyond this to build up a case for belief in the God of the Bible. But that is largely a matter of spiritual faith. It then becomes a case of "the Spirit himself bearing witness with our spirit." (Romans 8: 16)

By Divine grace I have this spiritual faith, and it inevitably controls my thinking with reference to the existence of God. My defense of my beliefs may for that reason be considered to be on a subjective basis, and I may be charged with mysticism. Those who apply this term, however, as though it were the *coup de grâce*, should offer an explanation of how the creature-Creator relationship could be otherwise.

Scientific apologetics had little to do with the placing of my faith and trust in the Christ of God, and the filling of my need by Christ. It was a powerful sense of need which was the motivating factor. Subsequent study in the field of geochemistry has contributed to my appreciation of the fact that God made this universe, and it has provided additional lines of evidence. And so it is but natural that I see in Nature the hand of God.

The two most significant areas in which the study of geochemistry has direct contact with a Christian philosophy of Nature are (1) the determination of a time of beginning for the universe, and (2) the principle of uniformitarianism (see explanation of this term in a following paragraph) as applied in geology.

The determination of the "age" or time of formation of various geological specimens such as meteoritic material, utilizing known radioactivity relationships, has made it possible to attempt a reconstruction of earth history on a semiquantitative basis. A number of independent methods of age determination are now being applied with varying degrees of

133]

accuracy, but generally with satisfactory agreement. The fact that various interpretations of astronomical evidence lead to similar conclusions with regard to the age of the universe lends a great deal of weight to the view that the universe had its origin about five billion years ago. An eternal universe can be eliminated from consideration by an extension of this argument. In a universe which had no beginning, but had always existed, no radioactive elements would remain. This may be considered as just one corollary of the second law of thermodynamics (heat energy). The concept of a cyclical universe, alternately expanding and contracting, is extra-scientific and therefore must be evaluated as an unproved hypothesis, or sheer guesswork. The conclusion that the universe had a beginning is in accord with the simple Scriptural statement, "In the beginning God created the heavens and the earth," as well as being strongly supported by thermodynamic, astronomic and geologic data.

The principle of uniformitarianism is axiomatic to all of geology. The meaning of this principle is that it is assumed that geological and geochemical processes which are operative now were active in the past, and therefore an understanding of these processes provides a basis for the interpretation of geological history. Orderly behavior in Nature and the existence of "natural laws" are a cornerstone of modern science.

The orderly universe which is so necessary to the scientist is one which we accept as consistent with the Scriptural view of God as not only the Creator but also the Sustainer of the universe. A chaotic universe would make meaningless such a statement as that of the inspired and scholarly Apostle Paul: "Ever since the creation of the world His invisible nature, namely His eternal power and deity, has been clearly perceived in the things that have been made." (Romans 1: 20)

Without order, *miracles* cannot be recognized. The works that Christ did, which were to bear witness that He had been sent from God, and in fact even the resurrection, can only be evaluated properly in an ordered universe where such events are not random phenomena. As the great geologist J. W. Dawson pointed out years ago, "In truth, belief in law is essential to the philosophical conception of prayer. If the universe were a mere chaos of chances, or if it were a result of absolute necessity, there would be no place for intelligent prayer; but if it is under the control of a Lawgiver, wise and merciful, not a mere manager of material machinery, but a true Father of all, then we can come to such a Being with our requests, not in the belief that we change His great plans, nor that any advantage could result from this if it were possible, but that these plans may be made in His boundless wisdom and love to meet our necessities." (*The Origin of the World According to Revelation and Science.*)

Finally, speaking of my own particular branch of science, the study of geochemistry teaches one to look at things on a vast scale; to think of time in units of billions of years of earth history, of space in terms that encompass the universe, of processes that involve world-wide cycles. The vastness of it all leads one inevitably to a new appreciation of the majesty of God. The non-Christian will at least be filled with awe and wonder, and finally may be led to acknowledge that "The heavens declare the glory of God and the firmament showeth His handiwork."

The sense of this point, and in fact a summary of apologetics based on science, is expressed in the hymn "How Great Thou Art" that has thrilled millions of listeners during a recent religious crusade in New York City. Perhaps the tremendous discoveries in God's Nature, in these late years, one following upon another in fast and seemingly endless succession, had disposed that vast audience to avid listening, and perhaps explains the worldwide appeal of that hymn:

> O Lord my God, when I in awesome wonder
> Consider all the worlds Thy hands have made,
> And see the stars, and hear the rolling thunder,
> Thy power throughout the universe displayed—
> Then sings my soul, my Savior God, to Thee:
> How great Thou art, how great Thou art!

GENESIS I IN THE LIGHT OF MODERN ASTRONOMY

BY PETER W. STONER

MATHEMATICIAN AND ASTRONOMER

M.Sc., two years graduate work towards Ph.D., University of California. Formerly on teaching staff of University of California; thereafter Chairman of Division of Mathematics and Astronomy, Pasa City College, and Chairman of Science Division, Westmont College. Member of various national scientific organizations. Specialist in historic development of astronomical and astrophysical theories.

WHILE a graduate student in the University of California I was asked to teach a Sunday school class of Chinese students, young men who were pursuing studies under government sponsorship. Some twelve of these students had gone to the pastor of the First Presbyterian church of Berkeley and asked for a Sunday school class, saying frankly that they did not wish to become Christians but wished to learn about the religion of Christianity and how, and to which degree, it had influenced American culture. The pastor thought I should organize and instruct this special class, and somewhat hesitantly I agreed.

I was immediately faced with the problem as to what should be presented to a group of this type. Since these young men had no faith in the Bible, ordinary Bible teaching seemed useless. Then I hit upon an idea. I had noticed in my undergraduate work a very close relation between the first chapter of Genesis and the sciences, and decided to present this picture to the group.

The students and I naturally were aware of the fact that this Genesis material had been written thousands of years before science had any of its present day knowledge and concepts regarding the universe, and the earth, and the life upon it. We realized that many of the teachings of people back in the days of Moses and for thousands of years thereafter were very absurd when looked at in the light of modern knowledge—knowledge available also to this group of students. Nevertheless, we "tackled" the subject with a will.

We spent the whole winter on Genesis I. The students took assignments to the university library, and then brought back papers marked by a thoroughness such as a teacher usually only dreams of. At the end of that winter the pastor invited me to his office and told me that the entire group had come to him saying that they wished to become Christians. It had been proved to them, they had said, that the Bible was the inspired Word of God, and they were convinced that their own books of religion were not.

I am now going to be very frank. Up to this time I myself was a Christian, but like many others I considered the Bible to be a book giving the plan of salvation and the necessary instruction in spiritual matters, but perhaps not reliable in many parts. I myself was as much impressed by our findings as were the students. From that day (away back in 1910) I have watched the developments of science very closely and have compared them with the Genesis account.

Take the very first verse of Genesis I: "In the beginning God created the heavens and the earth." We believed at the time of my Chinese student class that matter was indestructible. We could change its form, but it was still matter, and in exactly the same amount. Consequently it was the current idea that there had been no beginning to the physical universe and that there would be no ending. Our only possible agreement with the Genesis statement was that if there actually *was* a beginning, it certainly would take God to bring it about. No other power was adequate.

But now atomic energy has come into being, and we all know that mass can be changed into energy, and energy into mass. So now the idea of creation looks more plausible. Science has now set tentative ages for many things. Some of them are: (1) the age of the earth, (2) the age of meteorites, (3) the age of the earth-moon system, (4) the age of the sun, (5) the age of our galaxy, (6) the age of the universe, (7) the time required to develop the various elements, their divisions and quantities. These ages all turn out to be nearly the same—in the neighborhood of six billion years. This situation is so striking that many astronomers are now freely talking about the day of creation, and they set it at about six billion years ago. This information of course the Chinese students and their teacher did not have.

The second verse of Genesis I, in our class studies, was very difficult: "And the earth was without form, and void; and darkness was upon the face of the deep." In 1910 the Nebular Hypothesis held absolute sway in the thinking of scientific men. It had the solar system disc-shaped; Genesis had it shapeless, or without a formal shape. It theorized that the solar system had been a dense gas; Genesis has it void, or very rare. It fostered the idea that the solar system had been very hot, giving off tremendous amounts of light; Genesis says it was dark. In 1910 we could do no better than to say that we did not understand why there should be such a difference, and that possibly some day the difference would be resolved.

The change came sooner than we had expected. When the 100-inch telescope went into service Dr. E. P. Hubble went to work on the spiral nebulas. We were sure that the spiral nebulas were dense, disc-shaped bodies of very hot gas, rapidly rotating, and that the outer parts of each would collect to form planets and the central part would form a sun. Thus new solar systems similar to our own would come into existence.

Dr. Hubble found that these spirals were not gaseous bodies in our own galaxy at all, but were great aggregations of stars; in fact, galaxies similar to our own and far out in space, so far that they looked like disc-shaped bodies of hot gas. This discovery of Dr. Hubble's was a great blow to the Nebular Hypothesis. This hypothesis was based primarily on the photographs of these spirals. We could almost see parts of each nebula coming off to make the various planets, and certainly the central parts would make stars like our sun!

Soon after this it was determined that if there had been a disc-shaped body of gas, hot and rotating, it could not possibly have formed a solar system but would have divided into two nearly equal parts. All of the planets put together do not constitute one-tenth of one percent of the mass of the sun. Henry Norris Russell in his book *The Solar System and Its Origin* gives several other arguments against the Nebular

[140

Hypothesis. So the hypothesis died. It was rapidly followed by the Planetessimal Theory and the Tidal Theory. Both of these were short-lived.

An important question still persisted: What is the second verse of Genesis I talking about? Is there anything, today, in the far distant heavens, that is without form, rare and dark? No astronomer had an answer; we knew of no such astronomical body. There were dark spots in the sky where we thought there just happened to be no stars. We thought we were simply looking out into vacant, outer space.

Once again Dr. Hubble went to work. He went to work on these "holes" and proved to the world, through actual photographs, that they were not holes but dark nebulas. He proved that they were extremely rare—of very thin composition. They were certainly dark, and their shapes were as varied as the clouds which float across the summer sky. The problem was solved. The second verse of Genesis I refers to a dark nebula.

All present theories of astronomy bring our solar system from a "diffuse nebula," and most diffuse nebulas are dark. The only difference between a bright nebula and a dark one is that the bright nebula has an early type star close enough to excite it so that it gives off light.

The second verse now becomes very remarkable. How did Moses know that a dark nebula existed thousands of years before science discovered the first one? And how did he know that the earth came from one?

The next few verses in Genesis I describe the formation of our solar system from the nebula. They outline the collection of a large part to make the sun, which then shines on a smaller part, the earth, producing day and night. Today we know that the earth is too small to have ever been a star, as it is only 1/333,000th of the mass of the sun. The smallest star is larger than 1/100th part of the sun's mass. We do know, however, that the earth would become hot, and that most of the free water would be evaporated and make a very humid atmosphere. As the earth cooled off, much of the moisture in the atmosphere would precipitate upon the earth and probably cover it completely (Geology believes the earth was covered with water at this early period). Later the land would rise from the water.

The Genesis account certainly agrees with modern science. The breaking of the clouds as described in verses 14 to 18 occurs in the proper geological period, after the advent of vegetation and before the appearance of fish. The order of the appearance of life upon the earth—vegetation, fish, fowl, mammals, and man—is approved by science completely. If Moses by himself, or any other mere man, at this early age, had tried to write a story of beginnings it certainly would be full of errors. But now there is the authentic record, and there is not one single item in this Genesis chapter which disagrees with science as we know it today. I have obtained more technical and detailed translations of different parts of this chapter from nationally known language scholars, and in every case the agreement with science is still improved.

I have given only one of many scientific proofs of the reality of God and the reliability of the Sacred Record. Genesis I has been attacked by non-believers down through the ages, but still it stands, unmarred and majestic. I am convinced that it will withstand any future attacks by well-intentioned but mistaken theorists.

THE GREAT DESIGNER

BY CLAUDE M. HATHAWAY

CONSULTING ENGINEER

B.Sc.EE, M.Sc., University of Colorado. Formerly project engineer in Consulting Engineering Laboratory, General Electric Company, Schenectady, N.Y. Designer of "electronic brain" for National Advisory Committee on Aeronautics, Langley Field. Presently Chairman of Research and Development, Hathaway Instrument Division of Hamilton Watch Co. Member Sigma Xi, Tau Beta Pi, AIEE, IRE. Specialist in electrical and physical measurements and measuring instruments.

BEFORE I proceed to comment on my rational grounds for belief in God let me say that my belief in God is based for the most part, at the present stage of my life, on what may be described as experience. We should not discount too much beliefs based on experience, nor should we classify them as irrational, for to do so would discredit the Scientific Method. Such beliefs may better be called "super-rational."

Although my knowledge of God in earlier years was based more upon reasons which I shall presently describe, it now rests largely upon the experience of knowing Him inwardly, an experience or experiences which transcend or render unimportant the rational arguments. While evidences of this kind may be unconvincing to those who have not experienced them, they are perfectly reasonable to those who have. I have found that God, the personal Christian God, is the only concept which perfectly fits the peculiar contours of the human soul. In the words of Augustine: "Thou hast formed us for Thyself, and our souls are restless until they find their rest in Thee."

But now for a brief statement of the rational bases of my belief in a supernatural God. I would first mention the simple, undeniable fact, no doubt more often brought to the fore in this volume, that *design requires a designer*. This most fundamental rational reason for my belief in God is one which has been greatly bolstered by my engineering experience. After years of work in the development and design of complicated mechanisms and electronics circuitry I have acquired a tremendous appreciation for *design* wherever I find it. With such a background, it is unthinkable that the inconceivably marvelous design in the world around us could be anything else than the product of a personal and infinitely intelligent Designer. Certainly, this is an old argument, but it is an argument that modern science has made more powerful than ever before.

An engineer learns to appraise order, and to appreciate the difficulties associated with design which brings together the forces, materials, and laws of Nature in such a way as to accomplish a desired objective. He learns to appreciate design by being faced with the problems of design.

It was my job several years ago to design an electronic computer which would rapidly solve some complicated equations encountered in two-dimensional stress theory. This problem was solved by an assembly of hundreds of vacuum tubes, electro-mechanical devices, and complicated circuitry, and the completed "brain," in a cabinet about the size of three large pianos, is still in use by the National Advisory Committee on Aeronautics, at Langley Field. After working on this computer for a year or two, and after facing and solving the many design problems which it presented, it is completely irrational to me to think that such a device could come into being in any other way than through the agency of an intelligent designer.

Now, the world around us is a vast assembly of design or order, independent but interrelated, vastly more complex in every small detail than my "electronic brain." If my computer required a designer, how much more so did that complex physio-chemical-biological machine which is my human body —which in turn is but an extremely minute part of the well-nigh infinite cosmos?

Design, order, arrangement, call it what you will, can result from only two causes: chance or design. The more complex the order, the more remote the possibility of chance. Placed as we are in the midst of design little short of infinite, I cannot help but believe in God.

The second point I wish to make is that the Designer of the universe *must be supernatural*. I believe that God is supernatural because my philosophy permits the supernatural, and because as a physicist I recognize the need for a supernatural First Cause. My philosophy permits the supernatural because by definition the supernatural cannot be demonstrated by the natural senses, and hence it would be begging the question to deny it because science cannot demonstrate it. Furthermore, modern physics shows me that Nature is unable to order herself.

Sir Isaac Newton recognized that the universe was moving from order to dis-order; that it was approaching a uniform temperature; and from this he saw the necessity of an initial ordering or design. This concept was brought into clearer focus by the study of heat, which revealed the distinction between available energy and unavailable energy, or entropy. It was found that in any transformation involving heat a definite amount of energy was transferred from the available to the unavailable state, but that transfer in the opposite direction never occurs in Nature. This is the Second Law of Thermodynamics.

Boltzmann became interested in this phenomenon, and he brought his keen insight and great mathematical abilities to bear upon it, showing that the loss of available energy expressed by the Second Law is merely a special case of a more general principle which states that in every physical transformation there is a loss of order. In the case of heat, the transfer of energy from the available to the unavailable state is actually a loss in molecular order, a disintegration of design. In simple terms, Boltzmann's Extended Second Law of Thermodynamics means that Nature cannot design herself, because every physical transformation must be accompanied by a loss in design. In localized instances, order may progress from the simple to the complex, but only at the expense of a greater loss of order elsewhere.

The universe is a tremendous "mass" (physics) of order. Therefore a Great First Cause is required who is not subject to the Second Law; who is, therefore, supernatural.

[146

SCHOLARLY WITNESSES AND A
FEW OBSERVATIONS

BY MERLIN GRANT SMITH

MATHEMATICIAN AND ASTRONOMER

*A.M., Ph.D., University of Illinois. Formerly on teaching
staff of Northwestern University; Professor, mathematics and
astronomy, Greenville College; President of Spring Arbor Jr.
College; since 1933 President of Roberts Wesleyan College
and Professor of Mathematics, Physics and Astronomy. Hon.
LL.D., Greenville College, D.Sc., Seattle Pacific College.
Specialist in differential equations and boundary problems
in one dimension.*

THE answer to the question of the existence of God
is intimately bound up with man's accountability to his fellow
men and to his God, if there be one. Great care should be
observed therefore in deciding the answer. If there is a God,
then He is not only our Creator but also our Sovereign, and
we should inform ourselves about the conduct He desires,
both with reference to Himself and to our fellow human
beings.

It is significant that many of the greatest scholars in comparatively recent times have acknowledged the existence of God, either directly or indirectly. Let me quote a few of them.

Sir James Jeans has said, "Our universe seems to be more like a great thought than a great machine. I would say as a speculation, not as a scientific fact, that the universe is a creation of some great universal Mind underlying and coordinating all our minds. . . . Scientific thought seems to be moving in that direction."

Immanuel Kant wrote, "Two things fill me with constantly increasing admiration and awe the longer and more earnestly I reflect upon them—the starry heavens without and the moral law within."

Dr. Alexis Carrel, a Nobel prize winner, says, "Despite its stupendous immensity, the world of matter is too narrow for man. Like his economic and social environment, it does not fit him. With the aid of mathematical abstractions his mind apprehends electrons and stars. He is made on the scale of the terrestrial mountains, oceans and rivers. But he belongs to another world; a world which, although enclosed within himself, stretches beyond space and time."

George Romanes, a scholarly biologist, observed that in the animal world each different species reacts differently in its environment due to the kind of life it possesses. As a result of observing the kind of conduct that characterizes the men and women who claim to have committed themselves to Christ, he concluded that they possess a different kind of life. As a result he became an ardent Christian, concluding that God alone could perform such a miracle in human life.

And concluding with William James—this great American philosopher and psychologist put it this way: "We and God have business with each other, and in that business our highest destiny is fulfilled."

It is a commonplace to say that where there is an effect there must be a cause. Scientists are continually seeking causes, and behind the causes a first cause. In some cases causes may be readily found; in other instances painstaking scholarly research may be required to eliminate apparent causes and determine real ones. This latter method, by way of illustration, has been widely applied in medicine. Typhoid fever has been almost completely eliminated. Great strides have been made in preventing or curing respiratory infections. Life expectancy has been greatly extended during the last quarter of a century. Other studies are being made in the field of biology to improve the functioning of plants and animals. There have been many unpredicted achievements in chemistry by the discovery of new laws and their application. Atomic particles have gained a hitherto undreamed of importance in the field of potential energy. The discoveries in astronomy, made possible through the use of new mechanical aids and new atomic information, cause our minds to reel at the magnitude of the physical universe, the endless actions and reactions that are being observed.

All this and a great deal more is due to the constant scientific search for causes under and behind the observed effects. Cause and effect are inseparable. Effect and cause are intrinsically one. We as human beings and the world around us are an aggregate of effects, and under and behind that aggregate of effects lies the invisible, primordial Cause, which I call God.

Besides the "law" of cause and effect, we speak of other laws. All Nature functions according to fixed laws. New laws are being discovered right along. There are the subatomic laws, and the laws governing the interdependence of extra-galactic heavenly bodies. To discover them has required the combined efforts of many very scholarly men. But we are simply *discovering* those laws. They are as ancient as the universe itself. Shall we accept the theory that they are of material origin? The multitude of them, the harmony of them, the very nature of them, make that completely impossible. These laws are of higher origin than the universe in which they operate. There is, to my ordinary, common-sense mind, but one plausible answer, and that is that these laws demand belief in a Lawgiver, which I again call God.

And in my view this God is not some indescript, volatile, ethereal being; much less one of the imaginary concoctions that have sprung from over-stimulated minds in many ages and places; but rather the God of the Bible, believed in and described by prophets and apostles, and acknowledged by the great "main line" of the Christian Church. The Bible is God's communication, God's letter, to man. In it the statement is made that man was made in God's image. Man's being God's image made him capable of receiving God's revelation of himself as the Creator and Sustainer of the universe. God could talk with man. Man could even talk with God. And the first great thing that God told man was that it was He who had made him and the marvelous, limitless universe around him.

Besides all this, there is the testimony of millions of men, simple or learned, scientists included, all through the ages, that they have actually experienced the presence of God in their souls. What shall we do with that testimony? Discard it? Ignore it? The "joy that is unspeakable and full of glory" that multitudes have experienced, shall we file it away, out of sight? The faith of the martyrs and the missionaries that made them brave loneliness, hardship, persecution, death—shall we grit our teeth, brazen it out, tell ourselves that it was all a mistake?

As for me, I believe "that God *is* (exists), and that He is a Rewarder of them that diligently seek Him." (Hebrews 11: 6)

The first four words of the inspired Scriptures are: "In the beginning—God!" I would make them the introductory words—the basic theme—of my own personal philosophy of life.

A LOOK BEHIND THE "NATURAL LAWS"

BY EDWIN FAST

PHYSICIST

A.B. in science; Friends University, M.Sc., Ph.D., University of Oklahoma. Formerly on staff of University of Oklahoma, Department of Physics; since 1945 with Phillips Petroleum Company. Presently engaged in atomic energy work—in charge of low power test reactor, the R M F, at M T R site. Specialist in spectroscopy, radioactive tracer work, atomic energy generally.

IN this writer's opinion an answer to the all-important question proposed by this volume does not require a lengthy and involved discourse. The answer can be concise, and at the same time—at least in the writer's view—adequate.

In the realm of physical science the most nearly correct explanation of a phenomenon is usually taken to be the simplest one which adequately accounts for experimental observations. A set of assumptions may be accepted because they aid in promoting a theory and because they seem obvious or reasonable. Using these as foundation stones the structure is built. If these are found erroneous or inadequate the structure falls.

The theory of *probability* is well developed mathematically and finds considerable application in physics. If no outside influences affect the experiment, a flipped coin tossed a sufficiently large number of times should show heads as often as tails. A die when cast should rest so that each of its six faces are up an equal number of times. A predominance of heads in the tossed coin might be observed with practice in flipping it from a set initial position and with a studied uniform snap of the thumb. Similarly the die, skillfully thrown or weighted, can be made to show one number predominantly. The difference in the two cases is that the first is purely one of unbiased chance, whereas the latter has behind it an intelligence directing the action and consequently influencing the outcome.

These rather naïve, simple examples may be extrapolated to those of increasing complexity. Let ten, a hundred, or a million units act simultaneously to establish a pattern of behavior. Any deviation from a completely random result leads one to look for some cause or directing influence. A description of such "directed" behavior is usually designated as "natural laws." If, for example, one considers the behavior of neutrons, electrons or protons in an electric and magnetic field, each behaves in a way which can be described adequately and hence predicted on the basis of "natural laws." Their properties (characteristics) are such that they behave in a predictable manner. Or if light from a sodium electric arc is passed through a narrow slit and a triangular prism, two closely spaced orange-yellow lines appear. The energy released as light comes from the transition of an electron from a higher to a lower energy state in the atom. This can be described in precise terms of a mathematical expression.

But—and here is the important point; the core of the ques-

153]

tion —"natural laws" are merely a description of what has been observed and not intelligent, regulatory legislation. In itself this description is not a fundamental reason or explanation of a phenomenon.

In seeking to find the origin of the universe science has shown how, on the basis of present knowledge of nuclear physics, interactions of fundamental particles can explain the build-up of all the known elements. Starting with the proton and its properties, and some force to bring the particles together, all known elements of our present universe can eventually be produced. The origin of the proton, however, and why it has its specific properties is not explained.

Regressing far enough one must finally reach the conclusion that the existence of "natural laws," which describe systematics in the universe, is evidence of an Intelligence who chose to establish the operation of the universe as we observe it. Once the electron, proton and neutron were created, with definite properties, their behavior patterns were established.

Our finite minds, in trying to go back to —o in time, demand that there must have been a beginning—a time when the ultimate particles composing matter were first formed. With the formation or creation of these physical entities must have come the properties which determine their behavior. The Cause which created the particles logically also determined the properties they were to have. If the brightest scientific minds through the centuries have studied to learn, by observations of great complexity, the existence and behavior of the various entities, it must follow that the intelligence of the One who designed these in the first place surpasses the integrated value of human intelligence to date.

[154

The best perceptive minds of today will readily admit that man has scarcely begun to learn what there is to know about natural phenomena.

When we turn to the organic realm, the complexities of behavior increase enormously, and hence the rationalization of such behavior on the basis of pure chance becomes infinitesimally small. The principal building blocks of organic matter are hydrogen, oxygen, and carbon, with smaller amounts of nitrogen and other elements. Millions of these atoms come together to form even the simple forms of life. As one considers larger and more complex species, the probabilities of definite combinations on the basis of pure chance are inconceivably small.

Coming to higher forms of life, there are those which exhibit intelligence in plotting and carrying out a course of action which may be contrary to "natural law." That such should appear on the basis of a chance coming together of elements, that these should in turn develop, reproduce in kind, exhibit reason and intelligence without a creative act of One who designed and established such beings, is very highly improbable—is accepting a hypothesis that for all practical purposes is impossible, while rejecting a simple, adequate one. In the unaffected words of the writer of Genesis: "In the beginning God. . . ."

Simple words, aren't they?

But there is majesty in their simplicity—the majesty, in this writer's belief, of Truth Divine.

CHEMICAL LAWS AND GOD

BY JOHN ADOLPH BUEHLER

CONSULTING CHEMIST

A.B., University of Pennsylvania, A.M., Ph.D., University
of Indiana. Professor of Chemistry, Anderson College; Consulting Chemist, city of Anderson and private industrial
corporations. Frequent Lecturer on highly technical subjects
for Indiana Academy of Science. Specialist in synthesis of
amino acids, application of organic molecules to the quantitative determination of specific metals, detection of Cobalt
II by Succinimide and Isopropylamine.

To understand how chemical laws are related to
God, to appreciate the extremely finite nature of the human
mind, and to make us realize that humility befits even the
brightest among modern scholars, I must invite my readers to
follow me in a very brief historical survey of chemical science
—my special field. I shall try not to be technical and to use
plain English.

Ever since the dawn of civilization man has endeavored
to understand the changes in the material world around him.
At first his understanding of matter was vague and incomplete. Democritus, about 400 B.C., was the first to make the

shrewd guess that everything was made of small particles that were entities in their own right. Such an idea was a bold departure from the concept of the continuous nature of matter. It contradicted the sense of sight, and the idea was quickly buried under the prevailing mysticism of the age.

For two thousand years alchemy with its accompanying mysticism and magic attempted to explain the meaning of matter. About the middle of the seventeenth century, however, Robert Boyle adopted the viewpoint of Democritus and applied the term "element" to simple substances that could not be broken down into simpler substances by laboratory means. This was a departure from Aristotle's elements of earth, fire, air and water. In 1774 John Priestly discovered oxygen, and in 1776 Lord Henry Cavendish discovered hydrogen. A short time later Antoine Lavoisier found that air was a mixture of oxygen and nitrogen. He also reasoned that water could not be an element, because it could be made by burning hydrogen in air.

Chemical science was indeed making progress. In 1799 Joseph Proust, a French chemist, argued that pure chemical substances, like common table salt, would always be the same regardless from where they were obtained. Berthollet argued that salt from different places on the earth would be different. After eight years of experimentation Proust won the argument. Thus the invariable composition of compounds was proved.

A Quaker schoolteacher, John Dalton, in 1808 attempted to sum up all the accumulated knowledge of chemistry up to that time and to explain the constancy of elements and compounds. He postulated the Atomic Theory of Matter. He viewed the elements as minute particles called atoms. The atoms of any one element were the same. Different elements had different atoms. He also considered atoms indestructible. The physical and chemical behavior of the elements, he taught, was due to a difference in weight and properties in the atoms. He explained the invariable composition of compounds on the basis that elements united in exact numerical ratios for any one compound. Thus it became evident that chemical phenomena obeyed laws, such as the Law of the Conservation of Mass, the Law of Constant Composition, and the Law of the Conservation of Energy.

With these tools to guide scientists in their adventures the qualitative stage of chemistry gave place to the stage where exact measurements were important. Once the road had been opened and the direction pointed out, real progress began. When it became an accepted fact that law and order prevailed, the study of matter became a science. For the next half century or so chemistry advanced along the line of Newtonian concepts. From twenty elements in Dalton's day to more than ninety by 1900—that became the record of chemistry's growth.

Dalton gave us the concept of an atom as a hard core of matter which obeyed the Newtonian laws. In the second half of the nineteenth century numerous experiments were to reveal the existence of a much more complex atom than conceived of by Dalton. Beginning with Masson, in 1853, who passed an electric current through a tube that had been evacuated, followed by Geissler who used a stronger current and tried more types of gases, we come to the experiments of Crookes, in 1878. Crookes produced a more perfect vacuum in his tube and noticed a strange glow when an electric current was passed through it. J. J. Thomson showed these mysterious rays to be negative in charge, to travel with incredible speeds, and to be almost weightless. These rays were called cathode rays and the tube that produced them cathode ray tubes. Later these rays became known as streams of electrons.

There followed the discovery of radioactivity by Becquerel and the Curies. This discovery opened up a completely new world of subatomic particles. No longer was the atom a hard core of matter. It became a miniature solar system, with its major mass at the core or center, where all the positive protons were accumulated; and around this concentrated mass the negative electrons, units of energy, were distributed in definite patterns. The chemical and physical properties of the atoms became associated with the differences in the charges on the nucleus and the arrangement of the electrons around the nucleus. At first, attempts were made to apply the Newtonian concepts to the subatomic particles, but it soon became evident that the laws that governed the behavior of moving particles on the macro scale did not hold when applied to the subatomic scale. Thus it became necessary to develop a new mathematics, Quantum Mechanics, or the Calculus of Probabilities, to express mathematically the behavior of protons, electrons and other subatomic particles.

In 1927 Heisenberg enunciated his "principle of uncertainty" to explain why the Newtonian laws did not apply to subatomic phenomena. This principle of uncertainty states that "it is impossible to specify the position and velocity of a particle at any one instance." Every time we observe an electron we change its state; we change either its position or velocity or both. Thus we can speak of the probability of an event occurring but cannot pinpoint any single event. Consequently we say that Nature follows the statistical laws of chance. The reason we have such certain and predictable laws in chemistry is because these laws are really *statistical* laws. We customarily work with large numbers of ions or molecules in the laboratory—millions of them. In mixing our solutions each individual ion acts in an unpredictable, chaotic manner. Yet we can predict the outcome of the reaction with a high degree of certainty. Several hundred thousand ions may still be unreacted, but since our analytical balance is not capable of weighing such a small number of ions we regard the reaction as 100 percent complete.

Du Noüy points out that everything depends on our scale of observation. What would seem to us to be 100 percent reacted might appear far from complete on another level of observation. Thus a gram of carbon black when mixed with a gram of flour would appear to us gray, but to a microbe crawling through the pile it would appear as a pile of black and white boulders. His level of observation is different from ours.

The reason chemistry seems to obey the laws we have discovered is because we are really dealing with a statistical science. At the base of our physico-chemical laws is apparent disorder and chaos, but because of the vast numbers with which we work the statistical laws are applicable and exact laws result. Thus out of chaos comes harmony.

What is the directing force that underlies the laws of statistics? When one applies the laws of chance to the probability of an event occurring in Nature, such as the formation of a single protein molecule from the elements, even if we allow three billion years for the age of the earth or more, there isn't enough time for the event to occur. Only by postulating a directional Force with a purposeful end can we account for the harmony and order which have come from chaos.

It may well be that the Heisenberg principle of indeterminancy (uncertainty) may only exist because we haven't found a way on our present level of understanding to observe an electron without affecting either its position or velocity. Some day, when we know far more about energy than we do today, we may be able to view the electron with the same degree of stability as we view the planet Mars. For the present, the Heisenberg principle is useful to help us in our study of subatomic particles, just as Dalton's Atomic Theory was of untold value to the nineteenth century chemists. We must recognize that we do not know all there is to be known about matter and energy. In fact, we have only scratched the surface. It may well be that what we refer to as disorder and chaos at the subatomic level is not that at all. Our idea may be faulty and may be due to imperfect knowledge of this phenomenon and a wrong level of observation.

All through Nature one finds order and design. The universe seems to be heading toward a definite goal. This is evident in the order among the atoms. There is a definite pattern that is followed from hydrogen to uranium and beyond. The more we learn about the laws that govern the distribution of the protons and electrons to produce the various elements, the more we become aware of the harmony and order that exists in matter. Some day we shall learn how energy is put together to produce these building blocks of matter. It was Einstein who first showed the interrelationship that exists between matter and energy. Man has only begun to unlock the secrets of atomic energy. At present we are getting energy out of matter. Some day we shall make matter out of energy.

It seems that the universe is one, chemically. We have ways and means to examine many of the elements on the other planets that we find on earth, and they are the same. Even in the distant stars we recognize elements common to earth. It is the belief of present day science that the same laws of Nature that govern this planet also rule in the far reaches of outer space. Wherever we look, we find design, order and harmony. There is no doubt in my mind that a Supreme Intelligence has planned and constructed the universe, and is guiding its destiny.

If time and space would permit, to emphasize still more the marvelous facts of design and order, I would call the reader's attention to the water cycle, the carbon dioxide cycle, the ammonia cycle, and the oxygen cycle. All of them indicate a planning Mind and a constructing Power.

Although there are many things in Nature that are at present unexplainable and shrouded in mystery, we will of course not make the same mistake the ancients made when they conceived of "gods" to explain the unexplainable, assigning to each "god" his power and function. At a later stage, as science developed and many of the mysterious phenomena in Nature became understandable, and as the laws which governed their behavior were discovered, "gods" were no longer deemed necessary. For many even God became superfluous.

As for God, instead of considering Him, or the idea of Him, superfluous, or instead of classifying Him among the so-called unknowables, we should see Him and adore Him in the law and order of the universe. Man may be able to explain the

[162

"unknowable" by *discovering* Nature's laws, but man will never be able to *create* Nature's laws. God is the Lawgiver; man discovers the laws and gradually learns to interpret Nature. Every law that man discovers brings him closer to understanding God. God uses that method to reveal Himself to us. It is not His only method—there is His special revelation in the Bible—but it is an important one.

SCIENCE UNDERGIRDED MY FAITH

BY ALBERT McCOMBS WINCHESTER

BIOLOGIST

A.M., Ph.D., University of Texas; graduate studies, University of Chicago. Formerly Professor of Biology, Baylor University; presently, since 1946, Chairman Department of Biology, Stetson University. Author of textbooks on biology, zoology, genetics, and a popular volume, "Heredity and Your Life." Past President of Florida Academy of Science. Specialist in genetics, effects of X-ray on Drosophila.

CAN a scientist have the same belief in the existence of a God, and the same deep reverence for Him, as one who has not engaged in scientific studies? Is there anything in the discoveries of science that would degrade the power and majesty of a Supreme Being? These are questions which sometimes cross the minds of some who feel that scientists, in their extensive research work, uncover facts which tend to run counter to the teachings of the Bible as interpreted by some individuals.

A personal experience illustrates this viewpoint. When, as a college student, I first decided to go into the field of science I well remember the day when one of my aunts took

[164

me aside and pleaded with me to change my mind, for, as she put it, "Science will cause you to lose your faith in God." To her, like many others, science and religion were opposing forces—to embrace one was to exclude the other.

Today, I am happy to say, after many years of study and work in the fields of science, my faith in God, rather than being shaken, has become much stronger and acquired a firmer foundation than heretofore. Science brings about an insight into the majesty and omnipotence of the Supreme Being which grows stronger with each new discovery. Science replaces the paganistic superstitions, which often creep into our religious beliefs, with sound facts which can be supported by demonstrable evidence. Just as the discoveries of science have altered the practice of medicine from the days of blood letting and incense burning to our modern techniques of diagnosis and treatment, some of our ancient concepts of God's relationship to man have been altered by scientific discoveries. We know today that personal illness is not invariably a punishment invoked by God for our sins, but rather an invasion of the body by certain micro-organisms which obey all of the natural laws which apply to all living things. Our belief in God has not been weakened because of our knowledge of these facts—rather we have learned more about God and the world He has created.

One cannot study the works of any craftsman without learning much about the nature of the craftsman who created the works. Likewise, the more we delve into the intricacies of the nature of the world and its inhabitants, the more we will appreciate the nature of that Supreme Craftsman who created them. My field of study has been in the broad field known as biology, the science of the study of life. Of all the magnificent creations of God, there is none which can surpass the living things which inhabit our planet.

Consider a small clover plant growing by the roadside. Where among all the marvelous man-made machines can we find its equal? Here we have a living "machine" which unobtrusively, but consistently, day in and day out, brings about thousands of complex chemical and physical reactions, all under the direction of protoplasm, the material of which all physical life is composed.

From whence came this complex, living "machine"? God did not personally mould it with His own hands and shape every leaf and root on it. No—He has created life with the ability of self-perpetuation; the ability to continue the species down through the generations with all the characteristics which make it recognizable as a clover plant. To me, this is the most fascinating branch of biology and the greatest revelation of the majesty of God. Here we are dealing with a world of infinite smallness, because the pattern for the construction of a new clover plant must be contained within a portion of a single cell, so small that it can be seen only with a powerfully lensed microscope. Every vein, every hair, and every branch on the stems, roots and leaves have been formed under the direction of tiny engineers within the one cell from which the plant grew.

Moreover, these tiny engineers have the power to alter the pattern of their production at rare intervals and to produce an organism which is perhaps somewhat more efficient than its ancestors. There was a time when many thought it to be sacrilege to imply that any forms of life on earth were not in the exact form as originally created by God. Today, most thinking people have come to realize that the creation of the

[166

intricate mechanism of self-perpetuation within living matter, with provision for change in the face of changing environmental conditions, is a much greater achievement than the mere creation of organisms which can only produce carbon copies of themselves throughout all of time.

Scientists now seem to stand on the threshold of another extremely important discovery—the actual creation of life in the test tube. In an extremely elementary form, it is true, but they have succeeded in putting together the chemicals in the proper order to form a substance known as desoxyribonucleic acid (DNA). This chemical formerly has been a substance produced exclusively in living cells. It is the very substance of life, the hereditary material which carries down through the generations, placing its imprint on all life coming from it.

DNA from one form of life has been successfully incorporated into the protoplasm of another form of life, thereby achieving something in the nature of a transformation of inherited characteristics. What of this *man-made* DNA—can it *also* be so incorporated? If so, man would have achieved the essential creation of elementary life.

The final outcome of this effort still hangs in the balance. Many scientists are doubtful; others consider it impossible. But even if this should work out successfully, would this be anything to shake one's faith in God? Only if one's faith is based on shallow superficialities. To those whose faith is based on sound thinking it would only be another step in understanding the work of the Supreme Craftsman who created all of the marvels which man is so laboriously unfolding.

A deeper and firmer belief in God can be the only result of a better insight into truth.

NATURALISM MUST BOW TO THEISM

BY OLIN CARROLL KARKALITS

CHEMICAL ENGINEER

B.Sc., Rice Institute, M.Sc., Ph.D., University of Michigan.
Formerly Research Chemist with Shell Oil Company; there-
after on Chemical Engineering staff, University of Michigan.
Presently Group Leader, Process Development, American
Cyanamid Company. Member American Institute of Chemi-
cal Engineers. Specialist in chemical engineering catalysis.

THROUGHOUT all the ages of human history man has asked three profound questions: Whence came I? Why am I here? Where am I going?

Many hundreds of books on metaphysics have dealt with these questions. The riddle of existence is an age-old problem. The thesis of this chapter is that theism provides the most satisfactory answer to a rational mind. It accounts for observed reality better than any other view and leaves a smaller residue of unanswered questions than any alternative concept.

With regard to metaphysical beliefs, scientists in our modern world apparently fall into two major classifications. One group, undoubtedly the larger, may be classed as "natu-

[168

ralists." The smaller group may be referred to as "theists." This is an over-simplification from a technical viewpoint. We use the word "naturalist" here in a loose sense to describe that metaphysical approach to reality which presupposes that "Nature is the ultimate reality." By "Nature" is meant all phenomena, all events, that arise out of matter and energy acting in time and space. The naturalist asserts that all reality is explained by principles inherent in Nature, and that there is no necessity of postulating a God, as the theists do, to explain reality. Before discussing these diverse and opposing views, let us consider what is involved in the term "the world of reality."

Philosophers have loudly debated what is meant by "reality." The phenomenalist, the positivist, the idealist, the realist, the theist--all are sure to disagree. The writer assumes that the average scientist is willing to make a "common sense" approach to the problem and will not seriously object to the following description of what we call "reality":

The world of reality is that observed by our senses and conceived by our minds. Earth, sky, water, trees, animals, men, are all observed by rational human beings possessed of their full senses and reasoning faculties. A poor tenant does not doubt that his ever-demanding landlord is real (although he may wish he were not!). Such items as these (and the list could be extended indefinitely) all have real existence.

Now, in addition to external objects in our world of reality there are, for want of a better word, "internal" objects of reality within man himself. These may perhaps be expressed as the world of inner perception, of cognition, of experience, of feeling. Man is "aware" of himself. He is able to think abstractly. He is able to transcend time and space limitations and conceive himself to be something, some one, or some place which or where he is not. He possesses the ability to reason. He has sensations, and the memory of past sensations. Moreover, he anticipates future sensations and predicts, on the basis of past experience, what course of action he will take within the limits of possibility. He has volition, intellect, and desire.

Human beings have a sense of right and wrong, a standard of conduct. Man has a conscience, a moral nature, a feeling of obligation to himself and other people, an inner compulsion which suggests a pattern of conduct and attitudes. Such words as courage, devotion, bravery, loyalty, faithfulness, friendship, love—they are descriptions of man's nature, of the "inner reality."

It has already been stated that there are two opposing views predominant in our modern world for explaining what we have called "the world of reality." Let us, very briefly, explore the strength and weaknesses of each. No attempt will be made to *prove* one false and the other true, beyond all dispute. To attempt this would be presumptuous. Theism is not true because the Christian God can be proved by argument to exist. Our source of information concerning the Christian God, or the Christian conception of God, is the Bible. But theism as such, aside from the Bible, is by all means *plausible;* in fact is, as we hope to show, more reasonable than naturalism.

We first call upon the naturalist to explain the *external* world of reality. His basic assumption is the eternality of matter (or energy, since matter is a manifestation of energy). The earth and our solar system apparently do have a finite age, but the elements of which they are composed have always existed. By a very slow process of evolution life has emerged from the inanimate, and finally man has evolved. All of his experiences are the result of physico-chemical principles. The order and symmetry of the physical world are inherent properties of matter and energy. For example, a rainbow appears in the sky because sunlight is refracted into its component parts in passing through water droplets suspended in the air. All external reality is simply "matter and energy acting in time and space."

Internal reality requires a more subtle explanation by the naturalist. Our sensation of touch is explained by electrical impulses passing along a nerve fiber from the point of contact to the brain. The brain is a vast electrical network and the center of our nervous system. Our sense of morality is merely "herd instinct," or "enlightened self-interest," at work, based upon our experience that we get along better that way. A mechanistic or naturalistic explanation can be set up to explain (more or less) almost any phenomenon in the internal world of reality, as well as in the world of external reality.

Now let us take a look at the weaknesses of naturalism. In the first place, it affords no satisfactory explanation of the origin of the universe, or cosmos. There are numerous evidences that point to a beginning of the cosmos. The astronomical observation of an expanding universe is best explained by postulating a time of beginning wherein the component parts were in a dense state (or "wound-up" state). All galaxies and stellar bodies are observed to be retreating away from each other at a very great rate of speed. Many of the spiral nebulae seem to have unwound about two and one-half turns. Furthermore, the second law of thermodynamics (heat energy) is very strong evidence of a beginning of the cosmos at some finite time. This law (based on all our observations in the physical sciences) indicates that the entropy of the universe is increasing; which means that it (this law) predicts a time in the future when all cosmic bodies will be at substantially the same temperature. This can only be true if now, and in the past, they are and were not at the same temperature. It is true that they will never be at identically the same temperature, since the driving force diminishes as the temperatures approach equality. But this does not deflate the *practical consequences* of the argument. There is no satisfactory explanation for this "entropy clock" if matter and energy are eternal, and the cosmos had no beginning.

Naturalism also has difficulties explaining the world of internal reality. Physico-chemical principles may be used to explain to a large degree *how* our bodies and our brain function, but they do not explain *why*. Why does man differ in so many ways from the animals? Why does he alone have a "God-consciousness"? In all the researches of man there is not a single instance of any animal erecting an altar to worship. Is it adequate to equate brain with mind? How can we explain memory, conception, reasoning? Naturalism has no adequate explanation.

The theistic world-view answers these questions in a most reasonable way. There is a "Super-Mind" back of the order, plan and symmetry of the universe. This Being created all matter and energy at a finite time. He "wound up" the stellar bodies and gave the initial impetus for an expanding universe. He created the earth with conditions favorable to life. The odds against these things happening by chance are about one in a hundred million, according to Eddington. This

Being made man in His intellectual likeness—a spirit with a personality and a will. He implanted the God-consciousness in man. He implanted the moral nature in man, consistent with His own nature. Law and order exist at His behest. Beauty, truth, courage, faithfulness, goodness, love, and other virtues are derived from these same qualities in God himself. Man's mind is derived from God's mind, and is more than the material brain, which is the tool of the mind.

To answer man's basic questions, theism asserts: (1) God made man, and all reality; (2) God's purpose for man is to have fellowship with Him, and to honor Him with a life of perfect dedication and service; (3) God wants this fellowship, this dedication and service continued eternally in an after-life.

GOD—ALPHA AND OMEGA

BY EDMUND CARL KORNFELD

RESEARCH CHEMIST

A.B., Temple University, M.A., Ph.D., Harvard University. Since 1946 with the Lilly Research Laboratories, Eli Lilly and Company, Indianapolis; presently Head of Organic Chemical Division. Specialist in rubber chemistry, synthetic organic medicinals, organic chemicals development.

PROFESSOR EDWIN CONKLIN, biologist at Princeton University, has often said, "The probability of life originating from accident is comparable to the probability of the Unabridged Dictionary resulting from an explosion in a printing shop." I subscribe to that statement unreservedly.

It is my firm conviction that there is a God, and that He planned, created, and sustains the universe.

But I should like to be more specific. It is obvious that the word "God" means so many different things to the myriads of people who have employed it in the many languages of earth. When we speak of "God" do we mean by this (1) the universal creative intelligence and co-ordinating principle of Nature; (2) the personal God of the Hebrew religion, the One who was both the Creator and the Leader of His people; or (3) do we define Him as the personal God, revealed through the Jewish nation, who sent His Son, Jesus Christ (by whom He had made the worlds), to be not only Creator but also Redeemer of a lost human race? Since other religions of the world multiply the definitions without end, there must be a great variety of answers to the question—in fact so many, that we can consider only the three definitions given above.

It is well known, of course, that there are those who hold only to the first definition of God as creative intelligence, while others, the orthodox Hebrews for instance, embrace both the first and the second. The Christian, on the other hand, accepts all three concepts, and his view is in direct antithesis to that of the atheist who denies each one in turn.

As a Christian I hold specifically to the third definition presented above. I believe in the God who is revealed and portrayed in the pages of both the Old and New Testaments. In both Testaments He is claimed to be both the Creator and the Sustainer of the universe. Most of Holy Writ, however, is devoted to a description of His quest for a personal relationship between Himself and man whom He had created. In this connection it may be observed that it is highly interesting that not a single attempt is made in the Bible to prove the existence of God. The narrative begins with the simple statement: "In the beginning God—," and quotes King David, Divinely inspired psalmist, as saying "The fool hath said in his heart, There is no God." With the Bible simply assuming the existence of the God proclaimed therein, it is perhaps presumptuous for a scientist or anyone else to attempt to use man-made systems of logic to prove or disprove His existence. Nevertheless, let me tell briefly how the science of organic chemistry influenced and strengthened my abiding belief in God.

We will admit that we must believe either in a supreme creative intelligence in Nature, or as the only alternative to this we must believe that the universe as we find it has come about as the result of chance, and chance alone. To one who has seen the marvelous complexity and yet the pervading order in organic chemistry—especially that in living systems —the idea of chance is repugnant in the extreme. The more one studies the science of molecular structure and interreaction, the more one is convinced of the necessity of a planner and designer of it all.

That has been my own experience. While laboring among the intricacies and infinitely minute particles of the laboratory, I frequently have been overwhelmed by a sense of the infinite wisdom of God. So highly intricate are the organic and biochemical processes functioning in the animal organism, that it is not surprising that malfunction and disease occasionally intervene. One is rather amazed that a mechanism of such intricacy could ever function properly at all. All this demands a planner and sustainer of infinite intelligence. As I continue my labors, my belief in God is progressively strengthened and the attitude of unbelieving colleagues, anywhere in the world, becomes more and more an inexplicable conundrum. The simplest man-made mechanism requires a planner and a maker. How a mechanism ten thousand times more involved and intricate can be conceived of as self-constructed and self-developed is completely beyond me.

Many scientists will probably admit the high probability of some creative intelligence in Nature, and yet the gap between this admission and a definite belief in the Christian God has been bridged by relatively few. It is the conviction of this writer that the bridging of this gap comes about, not by the processes of scientific method, but by the exercising of simple faith. Such faith will reveal God as the "Alpha and Omega," not only of the "plan of salvation," but also of the entire universe. It will reveal Him, in the words of Robert Grant's majestic hymn, as "our Maker, Defender, Redeemer, and Friend."

Christian faith in a God who is both Creator and Redeemer is neither irrational nor subrational, but in a wider sense it is perhaps superrational—above and beyond the confines of man-made logic. Faith in this case must precede reason, for "He that cometh to God must believe that He is, and that He is a Rewarder of them that diligently seek Him."

THE UNIVERSE UNDER
CENTRAL CONTROL

BY EARL CHESTER REX

MATHEMATICIAN AND PHYSICIST

B.Sc., Notre Dame University, M.Sc., University of Washington. Formerly Lecturer in Mathematics, University of Southern California; presently Associate Professor of Physics, George Pepperdine College. Author of technical volume: "Vector Analysis." Member of Mathematicians' Association of America, American Association of Physics Teachers, etc. Specialist in vector analysis.

POPULAR conceptions are often misleading. It is, for instance, generally believed that science is like a brilliant and talkative old man who knows all the answers. Instead, science is like a young man who asks a lot of questions. He does much thinking and pondering. He attempts to keep careful, classified notes. The typical scientist is never satisfied that he has the final truth on anything at all.

Again, it is believed that science maintains a straight-line course in a chain of deductive reasoning. In reality, science may be likened to a climbing vine, ever trying to reach higher. The path of science is a devious, winding one. Carbon

[178

14 dating, for example, is today being scrutinized if not revised. Thus, the path of science's direction must be continually changed, and oftentimes it is necessary to go back and take a different path.

Mathematics, with which I have something to do, is like a flashlight attempting to light up the path, but the direction of its beam must continually change to conform to the direction of the path of science. I use the accepted principle in science which governs the choice between two or more conflicting theories. According to this principle, the theory which explains all the pertinent facts in the simplest way is adopted. This same principle was used, in the long ago, to decide between the Ptolemaic, or earth-centered, theory and the Copernican theory which claims that the sun is the center of the solar system. The Ptolemaic theory was so involved and so much more complicated than the Copernican that the earth-centered idea was discarded.

But although science has its limitations, its theories and conclusions have proved of inestimable value, also with respect to the universe and the God of the universe. A fair and impartial study of scientific phenomena has convinced me that God exists, and that He controls and directs the universe. There is "central control," and the controlling Power is God.

There is evidence that seemingly unrelated phenomena have a common explanation. This is seen in Coulomb's laws for the attractions or repulsions between two charges, or between two magnetic poles. By comparing these with Newton's law of universal gravitation I was struck with the similarities of these three laws. Each has the force proportional to the product of the two charges, pole strengths or

179]

masses, and inversely proportional to the square of the distance. To be sure, there are differences. For one thing, while two like charges or poles repel, two masses attract. Also, while electromagnetic waves travel at the speed of light, gravitational attraction travels at an infinite speed. But these differences show they are of different things, and impel us to study the whole matter more thoroughly.

This has quite often resulted in marvelous implications in other investigations. The Parity Conservation Principle, in a similar manner, seems to indicate a unity of purpose. According to this principle, electrons which are emitted from a system of oriented nuclei are emitted symmetrically in a solid angle about the nuclei. It was found, however, that they were emitted in a preferred direction relative to nuclear spin. Again, we note a break in the pattern when we study the neutrino. It does not obey the Parity Principle. It would seem that the neutrino knows right from left and communicates this information to particles with which it is associated in decay processes. These and many other instances indicate the origin and control of the universe by one God rather than many rival gods, as pagans hold.

Biologists will tell us a similar story, so far as control and arrangement are concerned. They find the greatest of efficiency in the formation of physical bodies. The blood corpuscles of the human body are of just the right shape and size to do the work for which they are made. The same holds true of other organs, parts and particles. In the world of insects we need only to examine the honeycomb in a beehive, among thousands of other objects, to find the same perfect arrangements and similarity. Every one of the millions of beehives throughout the world are constructed geometrically, with the

[180

greatest precision, to give the greatest efficiency. If this and a great deal more does not indicate the intelligence of the one Creator, the control and direction of the one supreme God, I surrender what little claim I may have to being a scientist.

As a scientist I find my conclusions concerning God and the universe confirmed by the sacred Scriptures. I happen to believe those Scriptures. I believe all they say concerning the origin and direction of this universe. Scripture and science agree. That is to say, Scripture wisely and properly interpreted. I have no use for critics who claim that because certain historical and archeological details in the Bible are undependable, for that reason we can hardly rely on what the Bible says concerning creation and Divine providence. Besides, who informed the gentlemen that those historical and archeological details are undependable? They have been caught in errors too often for us to accept their flippant assertions. The Bible account of the Egyptians making brick with straw was wrong, because excavations gave no evidence of straw having been used! Now archeologists find that the straw was first made into a "brew," then mixed with clay, and thus used for bricks, to make them harder. That is one of many, many examples of Bible critics getting off the beam.

Any present theory of the origin and maintenance of the universe which ignores or denies the Bible account either doesn't explain all the pertinent facts or else becomes hopelessly involved and obscured. I, for myself, prefer to be governed by the old, accepted principle mentioned hereabove. I prefer the simplicity of the Genesis account.

181]

THE VALIDITY OF RELIGION

BY MALCOLM DUNCAN WINTER, JR.

MEDICAL INTERNIST

B.A. in Zoology, Wheaton College, M.D., Northwestern University Medical School; three years at Mayo Foundation, Rochester, Minn.; M.Sc. in Medicine, University of Minnesota. Captain of U.S. Air Force, Ellsworth Air Force Base, S.D.; Chief of Medicine, 29th TAC Hospital, Ellsworth. Specialist in Internal Medicine.

THE problem of the scientific validity of religion can be stated, more concretely, in the form of this question: Is there a God, and is He personally interested in man? I consider that question basic—basic to our very existence.

Although there are many philosophical reasons why there should be a God and why He should or should not have certain characteristics, there are really only two principal, elemental approaches to this question. The one deals with natural science, the other is historical and archeological in nature.

As to the first: Earth and the universe with all their complexities, life in its various forms, and finally man himself with his superior thinking ability are all too intricate to have

[182

just happened. Therefore there has to be a Master Mind, a Creator, behind it all. There must be a God. Since man is the zenith of all about him it would seem likely that his God would be interested in him, and therefore be a personal God.

As to the second approach, that can be made through what for centuries has been known as the Bible. This is really a collection of writings, or books, which originally were known as The Books, or The Scriptures—a collective name without a modifying adjective, indicating that they stood apart from, and above, ordinary literary productions. There are sixty-six of the books, written by a large number of writers over a span of some 1,400 years, and yet they form one systematic whole, with one central Figure—the Christ. Notwithstanding the fact that it took 1,400 years to write "The Books," and many writers were engaged in their production, living in several different countries, the one frequently not knowing about the other, yet we find no contradictions of thought; instead, a marvellous unity. Besides, all the scientifically confirmable data of "The Books" have actually been confirmed by secular history and archeological findings to an amazing degree. So far as scientific data are concerned, the Bible *stands*—like a bulwark of the ages. And this same Bible maintains from beginning to end that there is a personal God.

On the other hand, *what* man believes, and *why* he believes what he does, is determined to a great extent by both his intelligence and his environment. His beliefs can be divided into those that are "factual" and those that are "theoretical." To be absolutely sure that his factual beliefs are correct, he would have to derive each of them by application of the scientific method. Obviously this is impossible because they are both too numerous and too complex. He accepts them as being correct both because they are accepted by the society in which he lives and in the books which he reads, and because they prove valid as he uses them in his daily life.

Theoretical beliefs often prove themselves useful and are usually valid in the ways in which they are used. However, for various reasons they are not accepted by everyone, and application of the scientific method to prove them cannot be fully carried out because of lack of basic data with which to work.

According to these definitions belief in a personal God is a theoretical belief. The scientific method cannot be fully applied in proving it, and there are some who disagree that a personal God exists. Although both of the approaches mentioned earlier point toward a personal God, neither of them establishes *by the scientific method* that He exists. Therefore the final choice of (1) belief, (2) agnosticism, or (3) atheism is left up to the individual.

The field of medicine deals with man as an individual under stress. It tries to analyze what he's like and why he reacts the way he does. Therefore a very brief review of some medical precepts may be of value in a study of man's belief in God.

All illnesses have to be evaluated in the light of two components, organic and psychic. A patient's basic mental outlook or psyche to a large extent determines his reaction and attitude toward an illness. The psyche is hard to change and in many people it proves to be well-nigh impossible to alter. The well-adjusted individual usually remains well-adjusted. The neurotic usually remains neurotic. Psychotherapy helps superficially to alter a person's psyche but usually fails to do more than that, and in cases of individuals with very traumatic backgrounds often accomplishes little or nothing. Although, for example, an excessively compulsive personality might be somewhat improved through intensive psychotherapy, many compulsive features will always remain. Suggestion may cure one manifestation of a hysterical personality only to have another crop up.

The Biblical statement, "Train up a child in the way he should go, and when he is old he will not depart from it," has proved itself to be very true. Man's thought pattern is hard to alter. He is to a large extent a product—and sometimes a victim—of his upbringing. Most children brought up in a certain set of beliefs will continue to adhere to them. If brought up in an atheistic society, they are likely to remain atheistic. If brought up Christian, they are likely to remain Christian.

Just because one has been taught to accept a certain set of beliefs doesn't necessarily prove those beliefs are right, even though he feels they must be. This must be accepted as a basic premise. All of us are prejudiced, one way or the other.

Although a detached attitude may be maintained with reference to many problems that face us, such an attitude is impossible when it comes to answering the question, "Is there a personal God?" The question affects all of us to such an extent that we all have been influenced to think about it in various ways since early childhood. We cannot escape it. Nor should we try to escape it. As a question which is basic to our very existence it is one which needs answering.

My own personal conclusion is that the question can only be answered through a step of spiritual faith. This step is taken after inductive reasoning leads one to the conclusion that a personal God should exist. Once this conclusion is made, God himself confirms it by giving the individual a personal assurance of its validity that is unshakable. Call it prejudice if you wish—my personal testimony calls it more than that. Belief that there is a personal God is individual in scope. It can be arrived at by inductive reasoning, but can only be *proved* by supernatural means. Faith in God is the basis for belief in Him.

Faith has been defined in "The Books" as "the substance of things hoped for and the evidence of things not seen." Sir William Osler—prominent Canadian physician who practiced in the United States and England—defined faith as "the one great moving force we can neither weigh in the balance nor test in the crucible." Belief in a personal God can never be achieved without it.

WONDERS OF THE SOIL

BY DALE SWARTZENDRUBER

SOIL PHYSICIST

M.Sc., Ph.D., Iowa State College. Formerly Assistant Soil Scientist, University of California, Los Angeles; presently Associate Professor of Soils, Purdue University. Member of Soil Science Society of America, American Geophysical Union, American Society of Agronomists. Specialist in soil structure and soil water movement.

City dwellers driving their cars through the countryside admire the field crops, and know that these crops spring from the soil, but generally pay very little attention to the soil itself. Good farmers, on the other hand, pay very close attention to the different types and qualities of soil, although it cannot be expected of the general run of them that they make thoroughgoing scientific studies of the substance that means so much for their income and livelihood.

The soil is a world of wonders all by itself, but only scientific study brings that out. I shall invite the reader to follow me as I make some very brief, cursory comments. He may not, without further study, understand every phrase or bit of chemical nomenclature, but he should understand enough to agree with me that the soil is a world of wonders, and he should also come to see something of the network of design

187]

in this wonderworld—a network of design that inevitably will lead him to think of the Great Designer.

Let us take a look at soil as a weathering product. The products of geologic weathering have been listed as (1) residual mantle, (2) residual boulders, and (3) soil. All are the result of the disintegration and breakdown involved in weathering, but by virtue of its role in the maintenance of life on land areas soil stands in sharp contrast with the other two categories. Soil—here considered simply as the mineral mixture at the earth's surface in which plants grow—is the source of important plant nutrients, and is necessary for the physical support of land plants.

As igneous rocks (intense-heat-produced) weather, the soluble bases such as calcium, magnesium and potassium are removed preferentially, leaving behind the oxides of silicon, aluminum and iron to comprise the bulk of the soil material. The phosphorus content is not greatly reduced, whereas the nitrogen content is generally increased.

The weathering of the original silicate minerals leads to the formation of clays. The clay fraction of soils, in temperate and cold regions, consists largely of crystalline silicates, with smaller quantities of nonsilicates. In the tropics free oxides and hydrous oxides of iron and aluminum may predominate.

An important property, or characteristic, of clay is the cation exchange capacity (electrical action). This property enables the holding of the soluble bases by exchange reactions, thus preventing the relatively low content of these bases from being reduced to zero. Cations held by exchange are available for plant use. So, the weathering process which causes loss of the plant-available soluble bases also provides an inorganic mechanism which retains them.

[188

Lack of space prevents a discussion of other plant nutrient elements. Let us, instead, ask the interesting question how the Great Designer arranged for the growth and survival of the first plants in geologic time. Presuming those plants to have had nutritional requirements similar to those of present day plants, it would seem that the soluble bases and phosphorus should have been ample. With nitrogen the situation was different. Relatively large quantities are used by plants, and inorganic retention by the soil was poor. How could the first plants have obtained their nitrogen?

There is evidence that unaltered igneous rocks may contain ammoniacal nitrogen to the extent of 80 p.p.m. In the absence of prior oxidative reactions, this nitrogen might have been utilized by the first plants. But there are other sources, too. There is, for instance, lightning. Many people think of lightning only as an instrument of destruction. But it is known that discharges of lightning form oxides of nitrogen which are brought down to the soil in rain or snow. The readily available nitrate nitrogen thus added has been conservatively estimated as 5 pounds per acre per year, the equivalent of 30 pounds of sodium nitrate (Lyon, Buckman, and Brady, *The Nature and Properties of Soils,* Fifth Edition). Since the same authors report that such an addition will more than supply the nitrogen requirements of a continuous sod crop, it seems reasonable to assume that the same additions to primordial soil materials would have been sufficient to initiate plant growth.

A further feature of lightning fixation is that the nitrogen fixed in tropical regions is greater than that fixed in humid-temperate regions, which in turn is greater than that fixed in semi-arid regions. Geographic regions are thus being served

189]

variously, according to their needs, by the Great Designer.

Speaking of the Great Designer—can the soil-plant inter-relationships just discussed really be taken as evidence of the existence of purposive design in Nature? This question cannot be answered apart from its implications for science in general.

It is doubtful that scientists would generally concur on a single definition of scientific method, but most would likely agree with Turner (editorial in *Science*, Sept. 6, 1957), that in broad outline science has as its purpose the discovery of generalizations (hereafter called laws) of Nature. To be logically consistent, a scientist who searches for such laws needs to believe that they exist, and it is impossible to deny their existence in view of the imposing array of laws already developed by the totality of science. In the spirit of free inquiry it also is logically consistent to ask *why* these laws exist, and why it is, as in soil-plant and numerous other scientific interrelationships, that the laws fit together in such a beneficial pattern.

At this stage it is recognized that we are approaching the border region between science and philosophy. How can we account for this pattern or order? It would seem that, basically, there are just two alternatives. One would be the assertion that the order observed is merely an expression of the direction in which development has taken place, starting from an initially random state. But such a proposition is completely at odds with common-sense experience, and is refuted scientifically by Boltzmann's "second law of thermodynamics," which all modern scientists recognize. So this author accepts the second alternative, which is simply that Nature exhibits order by virtue of having been designed that way.

[190

The existence of a transcendent Intelligence is admittedly implied, but it is felt that this is far more reasonable and satisfying than concluding that order developed spontaneously from disorder. Hence, it is felt that the soil-plant inter-relationships discussed heretofore are evidence of design in Nature.

The author recognizes that any design interpretation will immediately draw criticism from anti-teleologists (those who deny an intelligent purpose in creation). This is understandable if we realize that most scientists of today, by virtue of their training, are not only steeped in mechanistic tradition but in many cases consider their scientific theories as practically synonymous with reality. On this latter point Conant (*Science and Common Sense*) has written cogently, pointing out that one is well justified in treating scientific theories and explanations as highly provisional. Considered from such a vantage point, the violation of the anti-teleological dictums of a mechanistic scientific mentality does not seem forbiddingly serious.

As a matter of fact, there is teleology, purpose, design "all over the place." One cannot escape it, in the heavens above or on the earth below.

To deny a Great Designer is quite as illogical as to admire a magnificent field of yellow, waving grain and at the same time to deny the existence of the farmer in the farmhouse by the roadside.

SOILS, PLANTS, AND A 4000-YEAR-OLD EXPLANATION

BY LESTER JOHN ZIMMERMAN

SOIL SCIENTIST AND PLANT PHYSIOLOGIST

M.Sc., Ph.D., Purdue University. Specialist with the U.S. Soil Conservation Service; Professor of Agriculture and Mathematics, Goshen College. Member of the American Society of Agronomy, the Soil Science Society of America, the Soil Conservation Society of America, and the American Association for the Advancement of Science. Specialist in chemical soil research and soil fertility.

WE all turn philosopher occasionally.

We walk along a field of growing grain, watch our gardens and truck patches with their variety of vegetables, see the ripening fruit in orchards and vineyards, admire the autumn beauty of the forests, with their wide swaths of flaming colors, and we ask ourselves: How did all this come to be?

Jesus told His disciples on one occasion: "Except a grain of wheat fall into the ground and die, it cannot bring forth fruit."

Jesus was a first-rate Agriculturist. He stated, in plain language, one of the strange facts of Nature, namely that

[192

death has to come to a grain of wheat before life can spring forth.

There must be water present for both death and life to result. There must be a source of plant nutrients. The chemical elements and compounds are the raw materials which this new life draws upon and uses in the manufacture of plant food. There must be light, energy, to supply the power for growth.

All life depends upon water for its existence. As Parson has said in his *Conserving American Resources,* water is the "life blood of the earth." Most chemical processes relating to life and growth have water either as a reactant or as a product. Water acts as a solvent so that the necessary chemical reactions can occur. It is very abundant in most places, and the cycle by which it is supplied to the land and its growths and verdure continues to operate indefinitely.

All matter is composed of chemical elements. The source of the essential elements necessary for the growth of plants is normally found in the air and the soil. Where did the soil come from? How does it maintain the plant nutrient supply?

A fertile soil consists of mineral matter. But there is also organic matter present which originally came from the lives of other plants and from animals. This organic matter is in the process of decomposition, yet in the midst of the decomposition process plant and animal life abounds. These elements, together with air and water, make it possible for the life-giving processes to function properly. A soil composed only of weathered rock fragments is barren. Productive soil is alive. The countless micro-organisms, both plants and animals, may constitute as much as 20 percent of the organic fraction of the soil and number as high as several billion per gram of soil. Thus, soil is formed by the action of the climatic factors upon the solid portion of the earth and the addition of living products, in process of time.

But how or when did these processes begin? It is not enough to have light, chemicals, air and water for plants to grow. There is a power within the seed which becomes active in the proper environment. Many intricate but harmonious reactions begin to operate. The seed which began as a union of two microscopic cells, each of which is a complexity of elements and processes, starts a new individual on its way to maturity. When the seed is corn, a corn plant develops. When the seed is an acorn, an oak tree results. When the seed dies, whether it be large or small, a plant very similar, yet not completely identical to the plant from which the seed came originally, springs forth. There is order, there is beauty, there is harmony, there is dependableness as one observes the various growth processes.

There is also the possibility of change. Hybrid seed corn has all but replaced the open-pollinated seed corn. With the proper choice of seed, tall and short corn stalks can be grown side by side in the same field. Length of time from planting to maturity can be regulated and selection made on the basis of the length of the growing season. New varieties, more resistant to plant diseases, are continually being sought, and in many cases found (for examples, see *Agronomy Handbook* by Cutler). Potential productivity has been increased. The record yield of over three hundred bushels of corn per acre attests to this fact.

All higher plants, while different from each other, have certain things in common. There is photosynthesis whereby plant food is produced from carbon dioxide and water in the

[194

presence of light. There is the similarity of structure in that roots, stems, leaves and flowers occupy a unique position and have a similar purpose. There are certain responses to outside stimuli such as bending towards the light, death in the absence of light or oxygen, etc., which are common to all plants.

Who was it that established and set in motion the laws of genetics and plant growth? That question very naturally leads to another, a most fundamental one: Where did the first plants come from? Or rather—for a chance origin is logically out of the question, and the assumption of an intelligent originator is imperative: Who made the first plants?

For an answer let me quote from a book that was written at least three thousand years ago, and that is dealing with events that occurred at least four thousand years ago—the very ancient Bible book of Job, chapter 38. In the form of a mighty, heroic epic the Lord God is represented as saying to Job:

"Where wast thou when I laid the foundations of the earth? . . . When the morning stars [angels] sang together, and all the sons of God [angels] shouted for joy? . . . Or who shut in the sea with doors when it brake forth . . . when I made the clouds the garment thereof . . . and set bars and doors, and said, Hitherto shalt thou come, but no further, and here shall thy proud waves be stayed? . . . By what way is the light parted, which scattereth the east wind upon the earth? Who hath divided a path for the lightning of thunder; to cause it to rain on the earth . . . to satisfy the desolate and waste ground, and to cause the bud of the tender herb to spring forth? . . . Canst thou bind the Pleiades [a cluster of stars in the constellation Taurus], or loose the bands of Orion [a large constellation on the equator]? Canst thou bring forth Mazzaroth [a constellation in the southern sky] in their season, or canst thou guide Arcturus with his sons [the "Bear," a cluster of seven very bright stars]? Knowest thou the ordinances of heaven, and canst thou set the dominion thereof in the earth? . . . Who provideth food for the raven, when his young ones cry unto God?"

The answer of the Book of Job to the question of the origin and maintenance of the universe (and that naturally includes the plant world) is *my* answer. All Nature was originated by God, and He sustains it, incessantly.

As I continue to study and observe the workings of Nature in soils and plants, my belief in God constantly increases, and I daily bow down before Him in wonderment and praise.

MAN HIMSELF AS EVIDENCE

BY ROBERT HORTON CAMERON

MATHEMATICIAN

M.A., Ph.D., Cornell University. Research man at Princeton University and Princeton Institute for Advanced Study; thereafter on staff of Massachusetts Institute of Technology. For past twenty years Professor of Mathematics, University of Minnesota. Was visiting mathematician at Institute of Numerical Analysis and National Bureau of Standards. Awarded Chauvenet prize by Mathematical Association of America. Specialist in mathematical analysis; in particular, periodic functions, integration in function space, measure theory.

THE very question propounded by the editor of this symposium is to me proof positive of the existence of God. "Is there a God?" That question implies thought—ability to *think*. I cannot conceive of such ability without an enabling Power.

I am not an automaton, and my thinking goes far beyond anything that could be built into a modern mechanical brain. Logic could be built into an automaton, insofar as logic could be reduced to a system, but thought is different, for it involves the power to follow the rules or throw them away. Thought

197]

involves reasoning, judgment, appreciation of beauty, enjoyment of a symphony, and a sense of humor.

Logic can decide whether a mathematical argument is a proof, but thought can create the argument in the first place. It can invent new mathematical concepts and discover new theorems. Thought involves the possibility of self-analysis and self-criticism. A machine can be built to play chess, but it cannot chuckle over an opponent's mistake, or regret a mistake of its own. Thought involves something that goes beyond a mechanism or mechanical rules. To me it indicates that a mechanistic philosophy is inadequate to explain man or mankind. I can *think!*

I also believe in God because He has given me *emotions.* Have I ruined my case when I say this? Am I admitting that there is no logic in my faith, and that I believe because I am afraid not to believe, or because I get an emotional "kick" out of believing? Not at all! Our very emotional nature is an evidence of the Creator's wisdom. What would our lives be like without emotions? How long would the race survive without the sex urge and the emotions connected with it? Why is it that infant mortality is lowest when babies are loved?

I believe in God because He has given me *moral judgment.* The race has an innate sense of right and wrong, as C. S. Lewis has so clearly brought out in his book *The Case for Christianity.* Though our ideas may differ, we argue for our "rights" and assume that fairness and justice are not meaningless words to our adversaries.

My belief in God is also based on intelligent volition—on the human *will,* which has been explained as "the total conscious process involved in effecting a decision." *Will* is one of the three great divisions into which psychologists usually divide the powers of the mind (the others being cognition and feeling). I desire, I crave something; my intellect renders its decision; and my will carries it out.

In all these attributes and characteristics man is distinctly different from all other earth beings; they are profoundly related to the Hebrew-Christian doctrine of the image of God: "So God created man in His own image"— and the same statement repeated for emphasis: "In the image of God created He him." (Genesis 1: 27) The Apostle Paul undoubtedly had the same thing in mind when he preached to the Athenians on Mars' Hill and quoted with approval what some of the Greek poets had written, namely that man is "the offspring of God"—or, properly, and in modern language, "of Divine lineage." (Acts 17: 28, 29)

I can't help quoting Scripture in this connection. Scientific evidences of the existence of God can only *concur* with what in my opinion the Bible states originally and authoritatively. A child knows nothing of his conception and birth; his information, at maturity, is obtained by revelation and observation—by what he is being told and what he himself sees and observes of life and its activities. In the same way man's original creation by Divine Power is revealed to him by God himself in His Word. Man's own activity lies in the field of observation, where he notes a variety of human attributes and characteristics, such as I have briefly surveyed, that corroborate, or rather underline, the authentic statements of Scripture concerning the creation of man by God, in God's image.

Scientists are "great" at experimenting. I am convinced of the existence of God by experimental evidence. This of course is something entirely personal. But for me the evidence is stronger and more convincing than any mathematical theorem could ever be. Thirty-two years ago, in a dormitory room at Cornell University, the experiment was made, and the God whom I joyfully found to exist gave me a new outlook, new motives, new joys (also new sorrows), and He means so much to me that I would give up my position, my scientific standing, and literally everything on earth that I have, rather than go back to my former state.

And the Chief Performer in that very personal, intimate, holy experiment was He who once upon a time asserted, with the solemnity and majesty of truth eternal: "I proceeded forth and came from God." (John 8: 42)

Yes, there is a God.

LABORATORY LESSONS

BY ELMER W. MAURER

RESEARCH CHEMIST

*B.Sc., Iowa State College, M.Sc., University of Pennsylvania;
Research Chemist with the U.S. Department of Agriculture;
specialist in synthetic detergents. Doing research for improved detergents for specific or general soils.*

As a chemist I believe in a personal God. I believe
there is a "Divine Intelligence" who created the world and all
that is contained therein, and for me this "Divine Intelligence" and this personal God are identical.

It is impossible for me to conceive the law and order of
the universe as being the result of pure chance. The odds
are simply too great. Law, order and intelligence go hand in
hand.

Also, as a scientist I believe that God has permanent control of His world. He sees to it that there is fixedness and
permanence in Nature's laws. When I step into my laboratory
I know that the laws that hold true today will hold true
tomorrow, and the next day, and as long as the universe
exists. Otherwise my life in the laboratory would be a succession of quandaries; a life of uncertainty and doubts, rendering

201]

all scientific activity futile; in fact, impossible. For example, I can go into the laboratory and heat a beaker filled with pure water until it boils. Without the use of a thermometer I know that the temperature of the boiling water is 100 degrees (centigrade) as long as the atmospheric pressure is 760 mm. of mercury. If the pressure is less than 760 mm., less energy will have to be applied in the form of heat to cause the molecules of water to break away in the form of vapor or steam, so the boiling point will be correspondingly less than 100 degrees. Conversely, if the pressure is greater than 760 mm. the boiling point will be greater than 100 degrees. This experiment I can perform time and time again, and so long as I know the pressure I can predict with certainty the boiling point of the water.

The chemist performs wonders almost routinely by intelligently using this pressure-temperature relationship. By distilling at greatly reduced pressures he can obtain fruit essences, dehydrated potatoes, dried milk, etc. Our gasoline and oil industry could hardly exist without making use of this simple, fundamental relationship. In fact, much of our research and many of our industrial processes are, in one respect or another, dependent upon this pressure-temperature relationship. This relationship is permanent and can hardly be an accident of pure chance.

Nor is the periodic chart of the elements a matter of chance. It is a beautifully designed scheme of law and order in the universe. As the name suggests, the chart is an assembly of all the elements in a uniquely orderly fashion, with a periodic recurrence of similar properties (qualities, or characteristics). In the periodic chart all the elements are grouped according to their atomic numbers. The atomic number is the number of protons in the nucleus of the atom. Thus, hydrogen, the simplest element, has one proton in its nucleus; helium, two; lithium, three; and so on.

Arranged in order of increasing atomic weights, the properties of the elements go through a repeated cycle of changes. All the elements in any given horizontal row differ from their neighbors by one proton and one electron. In the vertical rows of this grouping all the elements have the same number of electrons in their outer shells. It is because of this similarity in electronic configuration that the elements in a vertical row have similar properties. Thus lithium, sodium, potassium, rubidium, caesium, and francium each have one electron in its outermost shell, and for this reason make up a family of elements with similar properties. Six of the elements, helium, neon, argon, krypton, xenon, and radon, all have their outermost shells filled in a stable configuration and for this reason show practically no tendency to combine with other elements. These six are all inert gases.

In a similar manner all the other elements are grouped in families with similar properties, with similar electronic configurations. This beautiful arrangement is hardly a matter of chance. Suppose that I were able to heat in a giant furnace an infinite number of protons, neutrons, electrons, and "atomic glue" (which holds the atoms together). What would be the odds of my getting 100 or so different elements, each of which had its own characteristic properties and would fit into an orderly arrangement such as we have in the periodic chart? I might as well ask, what would be the odds of my baking a mixture of flour, water, sugar, apples, cherries and peaches together and obtaining separate and individual apple, cherry, and peach pies?

If I were to walk into the forest and suddenly find a clearing with a cozy cottage surrounded by flowers and beautiful shrubbery, I would conclude that somebody built this cottage and planted the flowers and shrubbery. It would seem ridiculous to me to say that they just happened. And so it is with the elements, and the periodic chart, and all the laws of Nature. Simple logic requires that somebody planned them, and made and established them. To me this planner and maker is God.

Moreover, I have long ago identified this God with the God of the Bible. At first certain difficulties presented themselves in the matter of the Bible's scientific accuracy, but they were cleared away. For example, I used to ponder a statement that Jesus made in Matthew 5: 13— "Ye are the salt of the earth. But if the salt have lost its savour, wherewith shall it be salted? It is thenceforth good for nothing, but to be cast out, and to be trodden under foot of men." The parallel verse in Luke 14: 34, 35 seemed just as confusing: "Salt is good, but if the salt have lost its savour, wherewith shall it be seasoned? It is neither fit for the land, nor yet for the dunghill, but men cast it out."

As a chemist I reasoned that salt is a very stable chemical body, sodium chloride. Salt just doesn't go bad on standing around. There are two possible ways in which it could lose its savour: (1) it could enter into a chemical reaction and thus no longer be sodium chloride; or (2) it could be so badly contaminated with impurities that its characteristic taste would be masked. I ruled out the first possibility on the ground that Christ was too good a teacher to make reference to a chemical reaction or process that the masses would not understand. The answer, then, must lie in the impurities.

All the while I was thinking of the nice clean table salt that we take so much for granted. A little research brought the answer.

Salt was accepted and collected as taxes by the Romans from the people of the Holy Land. One of the main sources of salt for Palestinians, of course, was the Dead Sea, or Salt Sea. So oppressive were these taxes that the people adulterated the salt with sand or other earthy material (the salt to begin with wasn't our nice pure table salt). The government purified the salt by spreading it in big vats or tanks, filling them with water and drawing off the concentrated salt solution or brine. All that remained was the earthy, insoluble material. Indeed, the salt had lost its savour because it was no longer salt. It was fit to be trodden under foot.

And this wasn't the only way that salt could lose its savour. The surface waters of the Dead Sea, on evaporation, have a chemical salts content of about 31 percent sodium chloride, 13 percent calcium chloride, and 48 percent magnesium chloride, together with other impurities. The calcium and magnesium chlorides are hygroscopic (take water out of the air) and will thus literally dissolve the sodium chloride. A bitter tasting composition results. It was the custom to store vast amounts of this salt in houses that had earthen floors. In time, the salt next to the ground "spoiled" because of the dampness. Since it would be harmful to fertile land because of its salt content, no man would allow it to be thrown on his field. The only place left was the street, where it was trodden under foot of man.

Thus the Bible was proved scientifically accurate, even in its many small details—for this was just a lone example. And, returning to the larger aspect of the matter, this same Bible, rightly interpreted, to me presents a reliable account of the origin of the universe, as well as its direction and support. I have found nothing in natural science, in chemistry, that conflicts with the Bible. Nor do I find anything in the Bible that conflicts with science. The God of Genesis, I am convinced, is the sole answer to both the "genesis" and the unfailing, detailed management of the world.

CONCORD BETWEEN SCIENCE AND FAITH

BY WAYNE U. AULT

GEOCHEMIST

B.A., Wheaton College, M.Sc., Ph.D., Columbia University, New York. Formerly Research Fellow, Geochemical Laboratory, Palisades, N.Y., connected with Columbia University; presently with Geological Survey, Department of the Interior, U.S. Government. Member of American Geophysical Union and Geological Society of America. Specialist in geochemical projects.

MAN cannot believe in the existence of God without doing something about it. Belief in a personal God will affect one's behavior toward his fellowmen, his attitude toward life, and his concepts of the motivation and purposes behind the material universe.

Scientific reasons for belief would imply that the scientific method of hypothesis, testing and conclusion was the method followed in arriving at or confirming belief in God. Now, the scope of scientific studies is increasing; more fields of learning are being put on a scientific basis. Yet, belief in the

207]

existence of a personal God is not directly on a scientific basis since God is not matter-energy as we know it. Neither is He finite, so that finite mind and experiment can determine Him. On the contrary, one's belief in God is largely a matter of faith, although this faith derives scientific support from indirect evidences of a "First Cause," and quite probably of a "Continuous Motivating Cause."

Faith is not something foreign to one in any field of human knowledge, but must be exercised especially by the physical scientists. Life is neither long enough nor does one have the facilities to perform every experiment for and by himself. One generally performs a certain variety of simple experiments, enough to give him an understanding of basic phenomena and faith in the work of the many scientists that preceded him. Subsequently, most of our knowledge is acquired by written history of past experience. For example, very few have actually measured the speed of light, but it is universally accepted as a known constant. Likewise, scientists accept the validity of working hypotheses; models of things they have not seen. No one has seen a proton or an electron, but only their effects. The Bohr model of the atom is one such useful simplified picture which permits the approximation of atomic behavior. Again, our knowledge of the composition of distant stars and the space between galaxies is based on indirect evidence and experiments. It is clear that much of such knowledge for the individual must be accepted by faith. This is not blind faith but faith which allows itself to be tested at various points and thus strengthened.

A similar exercise of faith may lead to a belief in the existence of God. God has given through men of former ages a written record or progressive revelation to mankind. This record reveals God and man's relation to God. It describes man's condition, need, and the means of redemption. It is set in a framework of time and space, i.e., history and geography. The Bible is a unique book in many respects and permits testing at many points. It is truly remarkable with respect to predictive prophecy which in minute detail has been fulfilled centuries later. It has not, to my knowledge, been proved wrong in any detail of history or geography, although there are areas where our understanding is not complete. It has been the subject of much destructive criticism, but not out of proportion to the greatness of its claims. If one will take the time to analyze these criticisms objectively he will find that history and our growing body of information from archaeology have already proved many of these critical objections to be in error and to have arisen solely from lack of knowledge or understanding of the situation. These three areas (prophecy, history, geography) are comparable to the volumes of scientific literature in being subject to verification.

Just as faith is a necessary and normal part of one's existence, so the concept of God is essential to the completeness of man's being and philosophy. Some of the important areas of man's experience, though intangible, are nevertheless real and of great consequence. Many thousands of rational, reputable and well-adjusted men have attested to a conscious personal relationship to God and to the power of prayer (communion with God). Man's psychological, emotional and spiritual needs are thus met by this faith beyond himself and beyond all men.

It is largely accepted as logical to assume a purpose behind all of physical Nature. The concept of God as Designer and Creator of all things gives a coherent and complete picture for origin, design and purpose, and allows for any process which is known to have occurred. Mechanistic views do not consider the ultimate origin and attribute subsequent events to chance. Chance is called upon as a substitute for God to complete one's philosophy. But even from a non-Christian or non-religious viewpoint the concept of God is far more satisfactory than chance, and the marvelous order of the universe definitely indicates a God of order rather than random, uncontrolled chance.

The concept of the supernatural has met with unbelief in many scientific minds. Yet at the same time many of the same individuals talk freely of phenomena which are called "natural" but of whose processes they have no clear understanding at all. Obviously, to call them "natural" only indicates that they are repetitive, but that does not *explain* the phenomena. Thus acceptance of specific phenomena at any one point in time, whether natural or supernatural, may be purely a matter of faith.

Falling back on one's scientific experience, the question might be asked: Is it design or chance which is responsible for the invention and construction of a radar set of very limited automation? Is it design or chance which is responsible for a bat—yes, a bat!—with intricate, miniature and effective radar, which needs neither attention nor repair, and which can reproduce itself *ad infinitum*? Scientific man's experience has been one of design and causation, and he should logically be the first to hypothesize a Master Mind, omnipotent, omniscient, omnipresent, and constantly interested in the whole of creation and every infinitesimal part of it.

There are many phenomena other than those already mentioned which seemingly have meaning only by belief in God. Such are the possibly limitless space with its numberless stars and galaxies, and the divisibleness of matter into its ultimate fundamental particles, whatever these turn out to be; the similarities of all living matter as we know it, and yet the uniqueness of every fingerprint, every maple leaf, and every snowflake. There is also the vast extent by which man is greater in mind and in dexterity than all other earthly creatures.

We have indicated that belief in the existence of God is largely of faith; that faith is not foreign to any man; that nearly all categories of faith are not blind faith but intelligent faith; and that the testimony of many is of a personal relationship to God. This has been illustrated by a few natural phenomena from material science.

The quest for knowledge and the inquisitiveness which asks the why and the how of Nature are part of the endowed traits of mind. Once the scientist has exercised faith in the Creator of the universe this faith can only grow as a result of studies in any direction.

GOD IN MEDICAL PRACTICE

BY PAUL ERNEST ADOLPH

PHYSICIAN AND SURGEON

M.Sc., M.D., University of Pennsylvania; formerly medical missionary, China Inland Mission, and associate in anatomy, St. John's University, Shanghai, China; Lieut. Colonel, Ret., Medical Corps, U.S. Army; Director of Chicago Missionary Medical Office; Fellow of American College of Surgeons and author of several books on Medical Missions. Specialist in general surgery and missionary medicine, particularly in relation to the health of missionaries.

ANSWERING the main question of this symposium, I would say that I definitely accept for myself the existence and reality of God. My conviction results not only from experiences of a spiritual nature, but medical practice has amply confirmed what I had accepted by faith.

Back in my medical school days I learned a basic materialistic concept of the changes which take place in body tissues as the result of injury. Studying sections of tissue under the microscope I perceived that, as a result of the various favorable influences which are brought to bear upon the tissues, satisfactory repair takes place. When I subsequently entered

[212

upon my career of hospital intern it was with a degree of confidence that I did so—confidence that I understood injury and the healing process to the extent that I could be sure of a favorable outcome when the appropriate mechanical and medicinal factors for the promotion of healing were brought into play. I was soon to find out, however, that I had neglected to integrate into my concepts of medical science the most important element of all—GOD.

One of my patients in the hospital during my internship was a grandmother in her early seventies with a fractured hip. I had seen her tissues respond favorably as I had compared the serial X-ray pictures. Indeed I had congratulated her on exceptionally rapid healing. She had now advanced through the wheel-chair stage into the use of crutches. The surgeon in charge of her case had indicated to me that she should be discharged from the hospital in twenty-four hours to go back home, since he was fully satisfied with her prospects of early and complete recovery.

It was Sunday. Her daughter came to the hospital to see her on her routine weekly visit, at which time I told her that she could come the next day to take her mother home, for now she could walk with crutches. The daughter said nothing to me about her plans but went to talk to her mother. She told her mother that she had conferred with her husband and it had been decided that she could not be taken back into their home. Doubtless arrangements could be made for her to go into an old people's home.

A few hours later, when I was called to the old lady's side as the intern on her case, she was showing general physical deterioration. Inside of twenty-four hours she died—not of her broken hip but of a broken heart, although in desperation we had utilized all emergency medical measures that might conceivably restore her to health.

Her broken hip bone had healed without a snag, but her broken heart had not. Despite all the favorable influences in vitamins, minerals and immobilization of the fracture that we had brought to bear upon her condition, she did not recover. To be sure, the bone ends had united and she had a strong hip, but *she* had not recovered. Why? The most important element needed in her recovery was not the vitamins, nor the minerals, nor the splinting of her fracture. It was HOPE. When hope was gone, recovery failed.

This made a deep impression upon me, since it was accompanied by the conviction that this would never have been the outcome if this lady had known the God of hope the way I, as an earnest Christian, knew Him. I was stirred to the depths of my soul. As a medical scientist I had a strong faith in God as the Creator of all, but somehow or other I had put my materialistic medical information into a compartment by itself, as though it had no relationship to my belief in God.

Yet could this mutual isolation be justified? Here I was confronted with a patient who had, as it were, gained the whole world in a restored physical body, but in losing her soul, and in particular the hopeful outlook of the soul (for obviously her main hope had been anchored in the perpetuation of a close human relationship to her daughter), had found death instead of life, in accordance with Jesus' words: "What shall it profit a man if he shall gain the whole world, and lose his own soul?"

I was gripped by the realization that I must seek the simultaneous healing of body and soul through the application of my belief in medical and surgical measures together with the application of my belief in God, both of which beliefs I felt I had established on a firm scientific basis. In this way alone can I give my patient, I reasoned, the complete therapy that he needs. Moreover, upon careful consideration I have found that my beliefs in current medical therapy and in God eminently meet the requirements of a sound and modern medical philosophy.

Actually, my own experience happens to coincide with an awakening in recent years within the medical profession to the importance of psychological elements in the science of medicine. For instance, today it is recognized on reliable authority that 80 percent of all the illnesses encountered in general practice in our large American cities have a predominantly psychic causation, and that half of these 80 percent involve no demonstrable organic causative factors whatsoever. In this connection it should be mentioned that it is the concept generally accepted by the medical profession that these diseases with the strong psychic, or so-called nervous, component are not imaginary in any way. Their causes too are not imaginary, but are recognizable through the utilization of a reasonable degree of ordinary insight on the part of the medical practitioner.

What are the basic causes of these so-called nervous diseases? Some of the most important which psychiatrists recognize are guilt, resentment (an unforgiving spirit), fear, anxiety, frustration, indecision, doubt, jealousy, selfishness and boredom. Unfortunately, many psychiatrists, while definitely effective in tracing the causes of emotional disturbances which cause disease, have significantly failed in their methods of dealing with these disturbances because they omit faith in God as their basic approach.

Moreover, what are these emotional disturbances, these causative factors in producing disease, but the results and reflections of what God in the Bible says He came to save us from? God had long ago anticipated our psychic needs and had provided a perfect remedy for them. The psychiatrists have described in intricate detail the lock which closes the door of health to us. God in His Word has furnished us with the key which fits that lock in minutest detail, to open the door of emotional health to us, just as the notches and elevations on a Yale key correspond precisely to the minutest configurations within the lock as the necessary components for unlocking it.

Only God could furnish this key. Blind experimentation could never make the keys that open our complicated mechanical locks; it certainly cannot make the key that opens the door of the human soul. Also, only God can reveal unerringly the particularities of this key. The poet Cowper has stated the matter correctly:

> Blind unbelief is sure to err,
> And scan His work in vain;
> God is His own Interpreter,
> And He will make it plain.

What does God, as "His own Interpreter," tell us about this key? Very briefly this: That we are guilty sinners needing God's forgiveness through Christ, so that we may be restored to fellowship with Him and may be forgiving towards others. Sinners thus forgiven have the gift of God's Spirit within them to dispel fear and anxiety, and to create an environment in which frustration becomes impossible. Jealousy, selfishness, and kindred evils depart when His love reigns in our hearts. Boredom is swallowed up in rejoicing. Hope becomes a living factor—living and life-infusing.

As a medical scientist I have found that, equipped with this spiritual armamentarium as well as with my materia medica, I can cope with the diseases of everyday medical practice with real blessing. To leave God out of the matter is often to provide only half a cure, if indeed that much.

Thus, the great majority of peptic ulcers are recognized as due, as has been tritely said, not so much to what the individual is eating as to what is eating him. The patient's resentments must be dealt with. In dealing with them we face up to that basic forgiveness of the crucified Christ who prayed for His enemies. If we are "of Christ," we shall find that resentments and bitterness toward others leave us. They *must* leave us if we are acting in sincerity. This prepares the way for recovery to take place, especially if the spiritual transaction is accompanied by the antispasmodic and antacid medicines together with the bland diet which we usually prescribe for this condition.

Similarly, there are many nervous conditions in which fear and anxiety play an important causative part. When fear and anxiety are dealt with on the basis of simple trust in God, health is restored almost dramatically in many cases.

Space is lacking to give specific instances of recovery from disease which have followed forthright faith in God. I have described quite a number of such cases in one of my books, *Health Shall Spring Forth*, in which faith's appropriation of God's remedy for recognizable psychic failings has, as part of the medical program of therapy, resulted in striking cures.

The human body finds harmonious function when it is in

tune with its Maker. Without Him we become prone to *dis*-harmony and *dis*-ease.

Yes, indeed, there is a God! I know—by abundant experience. Broken bones together with broken hearts find healing through HIM.

OF FLOWERS AND THE BALTIMORE ORIOLE

BY CECIL BOYCE HAMANN

BIOLOGIST

B.Sc., Taylor University, M.Sc., Ph.D., Purdue University.
Formerly Graduate Assistant, Purdue University; member of
faculties of Greenville College, University of Kentucky, and
St. Louis University Medical School. Since 1946 Professor of
Biology and Chairman of Division of Science and Mathematics, Asbury College. Research Participant, Oak Ridge
Institute of Nuclear Studies. Specialist in taxonomy of animal
parasites, toxicology of trichinosis.

WHEREVER I turn in the realm of science there is
evidence of design, law and order—of a Supreme Being.

Walk down a sunlit lane and note the marvelous detail of
a flower, listen to the beautiful song of the robin, inspect the
intricate nest of the Baltimore Oriole. Did the flower just
chance to form the sweet nectar that attracts the insects,
which in turn insure the production of more flowers next
year? Is it just accident that small pollen grains will germinate
and grow downward into the ovary of the flower and cause a
seed to be produced? Is it not more logical to believe that

the unseen hand of God has arranged these things by laws we are just beginning to learn? Can it be that the robin sings, not only because he has a mate, but also because God enjoys his singing and knows the joy it brings to man? While daily innumerable songs of praise are sung by birds that never reach mortal ears, like all God's gifts to His children they are ready and waiting when man gets to them.

And how about the nest of the Baltimore Oriole? Who taught him that fine workmanship? Why is there such a similarity of pattern? To answer "instinct" is an easy way out, but is it an adequate answer? What are instincts? Some say unlearned behavior. Is it not more logical to see God working in these creations of His according to principles concerning which we have as yet only the slightest of clues?

Yes, I believe in God. I believe in a God who is not only an all-powerful Deity who created and sustains this universe, but a God who is concerned about His crown of creation, man.

This firm belief comes not only from the culture of Christian America but also from, first, the scientific observations of the wonders of Nature, and, second, from an experimental awareness of His presence within me.

All around him man finds unanswered questions. As he sought to find the answers he formed many hypotheses, most of which have had to be abandoned or drastically altered before any part of the answer, or answers, was found. However, answers *have* been found and continue to be found with each passing year. Unfortunately, increase in factual knowledge has not resulted in greater recognition of God. Rather it seems that man has felt that by explaining something he has eliminated the need for a God. If all men would only realize that these discoveries are evidence of a Supreme Intelligence behind the universe!

When we go into the laboratory and with a microscope examine a drop of pond water and its scurrying inhabitants we are faced with one of the great wonders of Nature. Here, an amoeba slowly oozes along, almost imperceptibly a smaller organism is enveloped, and even as we watch, it is digested, assimilated, and waste left behind. As we continue to watch we see the amoeba actually pull itself into two parts, with each half re-forming itself into a complete animal. Here we have seen one cell carrying on all of the vital activities of life for which larger animals require thousands or millions of cells. Evidently more than chance has been responsible for this wonderfully made animal, infinitesimally small as it is.

Nowhere in the varied fields of science have the physical laws been brought to bear more directly on the phenomena of life than in the field of biochemistry. Where the mysteries of digestion and assimilation were seen as evidence of Divine intervention, they now are explained in chemical reactions, each reaction under the control of an enzyme. But does this rule God out of His universe? Who determined that these reactions should take place, and that they should be so exactly controlled by the enzymes? One glance at a present-day chart of the various cyclic reactions and their interaction with each other rules out the possibility that this was just a chance relationship that happened to work. Perhaps here, more than any place else, man is learning that God works by principles that He established with the creation of life.

Lifting our eyes to the heavens we surely must exclaim with wonder at the orderly sweep of the stars. Night after night, season after season, year after year, century after century the worlds of outer space have followed their courses through the sky. They return so regularly in their orbits that eclipses may be predicted centuries in advance. Is anyone still asking whether they might be just accidental condensations of galactic materials, haphazardly wandering about? If they were subject to no laws would men put their faith in them to guide them across the seven seas or through the unmarked paths of the sky? Although men may not admit the presence and the power of God, they are willing to admit that these stellar bodies are governed in some way and are dependable, and are not free to wobble through space as chance would dictate.

Yes, from the drop of water seen through the microscope to the distant star observed through the telescope I marvel at the exact orderliness that I observe—so exact that laws have been formulated to express its consistency. Only because men have been confident that such laws can be formulated have they been willing to spend their lives in search of them. Without this belief and confidence research would be in vain. If each time an experiment was performed a different result was obtained, because the only controlling factor was chance and none of the physical laws applied, what progress could be made? Somewhere back of all this order must be a Supreme Being, for there can be no order and no laws without a Supreme Mind. As each new law is discovered, does it not cry out: "God is my Author; man is only my discoverer"?

As real as the factual evidence of science is the actual presence of God with me in my daily life. While we can photograph the stars and map their paths in the sky, or trap an amoeba on a slide and photograph it, no such tangible evidence can be obtained to prove the presence of God. Only as one will place himself in such a way that God can walk with him can he personally experience Him. If one will refuse to look through a microscope or to glance at a photograph of an amoeba, he may be able to argue at length that an amoeba does not exist, but the minute he sees one, or its photograph, the basis of his argument is gone. So it is with God. As long as one refuses to look for Him, or to acknowledge His handiwork with an unprejudiced eye, one can argue long and loud that God does not exist. Once the unbelieving man glimpses God, then no longer can he argue against Him as existing. This must be an individual experience, and all arguments are in vain if one refuses to look for God. "Unto them that look for Him shall He appear." (Hebrews 9: 28)

Yes, I believe in God—as God of the universe and as my Friend. I am aware of Him within and all about me.

THE ABSOLUTENESS OF THE CERTAINTY
OF GOD'S EXISTENCE

An Extended Epilogue
with Notes

BY *ANDREW CONWAY IVY, Ph.D.,*
M.D., D.Sc., LL.D., F.A.C.P.

PHYSIOLOGIST

Dr. Ivy is a scientist of world-wide renown. At this writing he has just returned from a flying lecture tour to universities in Europe and India. He is the recipient of decorations from many American and foreign scientific institutions. From 1925 to 1946 he was Head of the Department of Physiology and Pharmacology, Northwestern University Medical School; from 1946 to 1953 he was Vice President of the University of Illinois. Presently he is Distinguished Professor of Physiology and Head of the Department of Clinical Science, U. of Ill. College of Medicine, Chicago. Among the positions he has filled in the past are: Scientific Director, Naval Medical Research Institute; Commander, Aviation Medical Naval Reserve Corps; Consultant to U.S. Secretary of War; President, American Gastro-Enterological Association; and President, American Physiological Society. Dr. Ivy has written more than a thousand (1,320) scientific articles, and is one of the world's outstanding specialists in cancer and functions and ailments of the gastrointestinal tract.

Is there a God? Yes. I am as certain that there is a God as I am certain of anything. I am as certain that there is a God as I am that I am, or exist.

Belief in the existence of God provides the only complete, ultimate and rational meaning to existence. Belief in God is the only ultimate reason for the absolute certainty that man is a person and something more than a parcel of matter and energy. Belief in God is the source and the ultimate basis of the most inspired conception of the human mind, namely the original, natural Brotherhood of Man based on the Fatherhood of God. Belief in God is the only ultimate and absolute source of our inalienable rights and duties, because we are truly equal only in the sight of Absolute or Perfect Love, Justice and Mercy. Belief in God yields a power which guarantees that no absolute disaster can happen to the person who truly cherishes such belief. Belief in God is the only firm basis for faith in the permanency of spiritual values because such permanency resides only in the existence of an Eternal and Divine Personality.

The Existence of God Can Be
Logically Demonstrated

The existence of God can be logically demonstrated by the application of the principles of thought derived from the interaction of everyday sense experience with the machinery of the mind. The formal proof was first accomplished by Thomas Aquinas. The basic principles of the proof are illustrated by factual observations which many parents have made during the process of the development of the mind of a normal child. The existence of God has been proved logically to the satisfaction of millions of profound and critical thinkers, many of whom have been the greatest contributors to science and to human welfare.[1]

The Non-Existence of God Cannot Be
Logically Demonstrated

The proposition that "God exists" cannot be disproved. The proposition that "God does not exist" cannot be proved. The existence of God may be denied, as it has been by the atheists Karl Marx and Lenin. But atheists have not supplied proof that is rational in support of their denial. One may doubt the existence of something, but even then a rational basis for the doubt should be provided. I have never read or heard a rational demonstration of the proposition that God does not exist, but I have read and studied a rational proof that God exists. I have also witnessed what a true belief in God (which includes Jesus Christ) does to people and the dastardly things a denial of God (and Jesus Christ) does to people.

The proof which atheists and many agnostics demand for the proposition that "God exists" is that type of proof which would make God like a human being, or make Him as concrete as a statue, idol, or icon. If a God with such qualities existed, a freedom of choice regarding His existence would *not* exist. Since freedom of making decisions obviously exists in God's plan for man, it is a part of God's plan to permit a person to decide to believe or not believe in God. Man is free, if he so decides, to delude himself with specious reasons for denying or doubting the existence of God and to suffer the consequences.

[1] Footnote and subsequent notes follow this chapter.

Most atheists and agnostics, and even many alleged Christians, look upon God as a personality to be bartered with. They say in effect: "I will be good, if God will save my soul. I will believe in God if He will give us rain, or stop the flood, or stop my pain, or banish evil and injustice from the world. If a good God existed, I would not have a toothache." In other words, "I will believe in God, if He will construct or reconstruct the universe on the basis of *my* plan, my selfish plan, and according to *my* wisdom."

To approach God, to think straight and consistently, people must honestly rid their minds of their selfish selves, of cynicism, of bitterness, and of those things which serve as mental blocks to clear thinking, so that they can come to believe in and love God, and thus contribute toward the amelioration of the evil and injustices they talk about and deplore. In regard to the reality of God, it cannot be rationally denied that God is as real as the sustaining effects of food to those saints and sincere believers who have demonstrated by their works that they truly love God. Instead of complaining about the evil in the world, it is quite obviously a part of God's plan that we use our intellect and our freedom to make decisions to contribute toward the eradication of evil, so that "Thy Kingdom come, Thy will be done on earth as it is in Heaven" will become a reality.

Faith, Hope and Love Should Be
Based on Reason

My belief in God, who created everything, who exists inside and outside the universe, and who is interested in you and me, is based first on reason, then on faith, hope and love.[2]

I cannot possess faith, hope and love unless they are based on reason.

One should never retreat from reason. One should use reason, and use it accurately and aggressively. A faith which is not preceded by reason is a weak faith and is vulnerable to devastating attacks and to subversion. Religious faith not based on reason breeds bad character and bad conduct. One should *not* retreat from that reason and those principles of thought on which the actions and faith manifested in every-day mundane life are based, and upon which the thoughts and actions of our greatest scientists are based. Belief in God is based on the same principles of reasoning or thought on which faith in the future of material progress is founded; the same reasoning which causes you and me to believe the sun will rise tomorrow morning; or that tomorrow I shall have the necessities of life; or I shall be alive; or I shall enjoy my work. If reasoning is the basis of material progress, why should it not be used for spiritual and moral progress? Every-one should be able to state courageously the reasoning on which their religious faith is based and to demonstrate the sincerity of their faith by good works.[3]

If you cannot prove the existence of God satisfactorily, then you have to accept God on the basis of faith, or by saying that the existence of God is self-evident, as Thomas Jefferson did when he wrote the "heart" of the Declaration of Independence, as follows: "We hold these truths to be self-evident, that all men are created equal, that they are endowed by their Creator with certain inalienable rights, that among these are life, liberty and the pursuit of happiness; that to secure these rights governments are instituted among men, deriving their just powers from the consent of the governed."

[228

That is the profound statement of religious, moral and political faith upon which the constitution and government of the United States are based. The United States was the first secular government ever to be so based. And Thomas Jefferson and the other founders of the United States had impeccable reasons upon which to base such a faith.[4]

However, even when people say that they accept the existence of God on the basis of faith, it will be found that their faith is based on some antecedent knowledge, experience, or reasons. Some antecedent knowledge or reason is indispensable for faith in anything. To say that the existence of God is self-evident, amounts to saying that I cannot scientifically or formally demonstrate the fact because of lack of formal education, or because I have never organized my reasons, or because I am not ready or it is not appropriate to present reasons now. I have never found a person who when urged could not give a reason why he or she believed or should believe in God. The reason given has always been to the effect that "Someone had to make the world and the laws which run it," or, "There cannot be a machine without a maker." That is a basic truth understood by every normal child and adult.

The Development of the First Principles in the Mind of a Child

When I was three years old, as is true of most three-to-five-year-old children, I asked my father and mother: "Who made me?" "Who made the birds?" "Who made our cow?" "Who made the world?" The facts of life, or my sense experience, had so interacted with my mind while it had been

229]

developing that my young unsophisticated intellect had concluded that there cannot be a "machine without a maker." My intellect had moved the appropriate part of my brain to inquire beyond the immediate facts, namely, that there is a me, a bird, a cow, and had in addition concluded that there cannot be a me, a bird, a cow without a *sufficient cause*, a maker.

My simple, naïve, unsophisticated, unconfused, non-frustrated, non-neurotic, rational mind had discovered and expressed the most basic philosophical and scientific principles of existence and thought ever conceived by the mind of man.

The machinery for the development of mind in my brain had so interacted (or was conjoined) with sense experience (the material cause) as to develop sufficient mind or intellect to produce a *sense of being,* or a sense of "I am," or "this is me." It had also produced a *sense of non-being:* "I am not a bird, or a cow, or a world." In other words, my mind had expressed the fact or principle of *being and non-being.* It had also expressed the concept of *a part and a whole,* and that the *whole is greater than a part.*

Not long after a sense of being and non-being develops, the child becomes aware of the *first principle of thought,* namely, *"We cannot affirm and deny a thing at the same time."* The little boy says: "I am Tom" and "That is my sister Mary." The intellect of the little boy is too rational to say, except as a joke: "I am Mary and my sister is Tom." The child also soon discovers that it is incorrect to say that a square is round. The child realizes that a square has a "sufficient reason," and its sufficient reason makes it a square and makes it intelligible.

This knowledge of the child and the fact that the child has inquired "Who made me?" and "Who made the world?" demonstrate the discovery by the child of the *basic principle of causality.*[5] This principle is also expressed as: "the law of causation"; "there cannot be an effect without a cause"; "there cannot be a machine without a maker"; "for every change there is a cause." The thinking moves as a causal chain from the judgment of "the existence of me" and "of the world" to the existence of God as the Prime Cause; or from the existence of motion to the Prime Mover. Another means of expressing the trend of thought is: Design is evident; design must have a designer; the designer must be a personality of infinite qualities; and that personality is God. So compelling is the natural law of the relation of cause and effect that the developing mind of the three-to-five-year-old child realizes that there must be a Creator.

I have dedicated my life as a scientist to look for the cause beyond the immediately known facts. My mind as it has been developed by sense experiences (and their correlation) insists on looking beyond the immediate facts of life to discover valuable new facts or truth regarding the material and spiritual aspects of existence. In my search I have read and studied in the field of Natural Science, or of *"the world as it actually is,"* and in the field of Moral, Ethical and Religious Science, or *"the world as it ought to be."* I have found that many excellent writers, many who are known as philosophers, and many otherwise excellent thinkers either have made subtle and sometimes obvious errors which stir up dust, or set up a barrier against looking beyond the immediate facts, or have ignored the immediate and well known facts. The scientist who does such things in his laboratory places a barrier against his progress. It is by recognizing the known facts, by looking beyond them in the laboratory of material and spiritual values, of law and order, by being guided by the reason (ratio) in natural law, and by being energized by faith, hope, and love of the truth, that all progress is made.[6]

The Principle of Causality

A number of years ago several businessmen, a very prominent scientist, whom I had heard state that he was an atheist, and I were seated about a dinner table. Conversation lagged and one of the businessmen said, "I have read that most scientists are atheists. Is that correct?"

The businessman looked at me, and I answered in effect as follows: "I do not believe that statement is correct. In fact, I have found in reading and discussions that the greatest benefactors of mankind in the field of science have not been atheists. Many have been misquoted or misinterpreted." I continued: "Atheism or atheistic materialism is contrary to the way the scientist thinks, works, and lives. He operates on the basis of the principle that *there cannot be a machine without a maker.* He uses reason on the basis of the known facts; he exercises faith and hope when he enters his laboratory. And most scientists work for the love of knowledge and love of man and God. Yes, the scientist uses mechanism *as a tool;* he talks about *the machinery of the body.* But he does his research on the basis of the principle of causality, of cause and effect, of the unity and the law and order of the universe. As in the case of everyone else, every decision is made, every thoughtful act is performed, on the basis of faith in the principle of causality.

[232

"In the science of physiology, when one studies growth, development, maintenance, and repair of the body, it is found that each cell almost without exception 'knows' its role in carrying out design or purpose for the welfare of the body as a whole. In the nervous system the simple reflex actions manifest *purposefulness* as one of their basic characteristics. On further study the inescapable conclusion is reached that the inherited machinery for the development of mind has been so constructed that when it reacts with sense experiences sufficiently, the principle of causality is an inevitable result. In other words, the machinery responsible for the purposeful nature of the reactions of all organisms becomes more and more specialized until the sense of consciousness [discriminative awareness] becomes possible as a result of the interaction of sense experience with the machinery involved in the development of mind.

"With the further development of discriminative awareness a *sense of priority,* or *sufficient cause,* results. Or, starting with the *purposeful nature* of the reactions of single cells, and given the possibility of an evolutionary process which would result in more and more awareness of the environment, one can logically predict the development of discriminative awareness followed by the formation of the judgment of the law of causation, the consequence of which has been the achievement by man of a greater and greater control over his environment.

"In the science of physiology, the gills of fish demonstrate the priority of water; the wings of the bird and the lungs of man demonstrate the priority of air; the eyes of man the priority of light; scientific curiosity the priority of facts; the presence of life the priority of a natural law providing for the production of life. Now, I ask: Does deep insight, great clear rational thinking, great courage, great duty, great faith, great love demonstrate the priority of nothing? *It is preposterous to argue that the most profound thoughts, sentiments and actions of man argue the priority of nothing.* They demonstrate the prior existence of a Superior Mind, a Creator who is revealed in the world of experience to those who do not erect a barrier to the search for that Superior Mind or Creator.

"The law of causality cannot be disproved. Without its operation all living things would die. The human mind cannot function except on the basis of causality. I submit that the law of causality is something real.

"I have heard a few scientists say that causality ends where metaphysics or application of the principles of thought begin.[7] I maintain that it is irrational to apply the basic principles of thought, of causality, or priority, as it suits one purpose and then dismiss it because one does not want to be bothered with it. The addition of a metaphysical link into the causal chain is not contrary to logic. We do it repeatedly in science and everyday life. Whether the link turns out to be the truth is another question. But one never finds out whether the link represents the truth unless the link is forged into place and the search started and seriously continued. The forging of such a link is the only way the searcher may be tied to the truth and the Ultimate Truth.[8]

"It appears that the atheists, or the agnostics with a *barren* doubt, have a blind spot, an anesthetized area in their minds which prevents them from realizing that our entire organized non-living and living universe becomes incomprehensible without a firm faith in the existence of God. As Einstein has written: 'The man who regards his own life and that of his fellow creatures as meaningless is not merely unfortunate but almost disqualified for life.' I shall add that the only reason that he is not entirely disqualified for life is the hope, based on faith and reason, that he may be saved or reborn and start rethinking life as a child."

I then turned to my fellow scientist whose critical ability I and most everyone admired and asked: "Is what I have said correct?" He replied: "Yes, but the important question is —what kind of a God?"

I agreed that the first and most important question which confronts a thoughtful person is: "Is there a God?" The second is: "What kind of a God?" The third is: "What is the purpose in living?" And the fourth is: "What is right and wrong?"

I then said: "God as a Creator and Designer *only*, falls short of the Christian conception of God. I shall give you my answer to the second question, which basically is the Christian conception of theism. To do this clearly and concisely, I shall continue with the analogy of 'the machine and the maker.' Before doing so I should say again that Christian faith goes beyond but does not contradict the truth which reason can demonstrate. When a rational maker makes a machine he has a design and purpose for it; and while making the machine he puts much of his spiritual or mental self into the machine; and then, after completing the machine, he has a sentiment for it and is interested in how it operates. I cannot conceive of a rational Creator to whom this analogy would *not* be applicable. The Creator, as demonstrated by His works, may be judged to be *supremely rational*. You should note that I believe in a God who, when people let Him enter

235]

their minds and hearts, builds good character and conduct, gives them noble purposes, and endows them with a spirit of love of God and of man."

It was 2:00 P. M., luncheon period was exhausted, and the conversation ended.

Space in this book and time do not permit a complete discussion of the question we started out with. However, a few more points should be made before my answer to the question "Is there a God?" is completed.

The Qualities of God

The qualities of God were considered at great length on the basis of logical analysis by the Scholastic or Classical philosophers. Through the use of logic it was concluded that God had certain qualities.[9] The following is an incomplete sum mary of these qualities:

God is eternal and everlasting; is not matter; is not a body; is not an accident; is Divine perfection; is the good of every good; knows evil and evils; cannot be evil; cannot will evil; hates nothing; is infinite; is the purest truth; knows the infinite and all things; in God there is love and free choice; in God there are no passions of appetites; in God there are moral virtues which deal with actions and contemplative virtues.

These qualities of God largely conform with those found in the Bible, particularly with those in the New Testament. But most of the qualities of God provided in the Bible are presented on an authoritative or self-evident, and not on a logical basis.

Moral Causality Plus Free Choice

There are many reasons for believing in God. One which

should never be overlooked is what I term *moral causality plus free choice.* By free choice I mean freedom to make decisions.

The spiritual and moral aspects of man's life—what he ought to do—is of vastly greater importance for man's well-being than is his knowledge and control of non-human Nature. The knowledge of Natural Science increases our understanding of the world in which we live and our means to improve the production and distribution of the necessities and comforts of life, and to decrease suffering and prolong life. The greatest problem, however, in the world today is a moral and religious problem, namely, how to use atomic energy for the welfare rather than the destruction of human beings. The greatest problems which have always confronted the individual and society have been moral, namely, to make the right decisions.

All around us we find Physical Nature governed by inexorable laws. The same holds for Animal Nature in the wild. But Human Nature has been created *par excellence* with freedom to make decisions. Or, human society has been created as a society of souls or persons with freedom to make decisions, to eat or not to eat of "the tree of knowledge." And if we do not obey the moral law of God we suffer the consequences.[10] Obviously, if Physical Nature had freedom of choice, freedom of choice by man could not exist; all would be chaos.

The study of the behavior of animals reveals that the two general natural laws which govern the conduct of all living things below man are: (1) survival of self; (2) survival of the species. Very little reflection demonstrates that if such laws were not paramount, no species would survive very long. Unlearned reflex behavior appears to control the conduct of

237]

lower animals almost entirely, but the higher one goes in the animal kingdom, the more learned behavior operates. But it is doubtful whether freedom to make a decision, as it occurs in man, is manifested to any extent below man; if so, it is quite limited. So, in Animal Nature, the individual is forced to have respect or "love" for his body and not injure it, except to protect and maintain him or herself, or his or her species. In the intra-species and inter-species relations of animals the principle of expediency, the "law of the jungle," "might makes right," operates. A "peck order" is found from "monkeys" downward as far as it has been studied carefully. A dictatorship or totalitarianism appears to be required, especially among all animals that form societies (flocks, colonies, herds). The point is that there are laws of behavior in lower animals which are practically inexorable.

The history of man reveals the operation of the natural law of the animals plus the appearance of certain additions: first, the feeling of awe for the mysterious; second, the feeling of guilt or oughtness (conscience); and third, a judgment that the power which awes condemns those actions or decisions which cause guilt.

Thus, it is observed that a causal chain from the physical world to the lower animals and then to the higher animals has resulted in the production in man of a high order of freedom of decision, which has resulted in a greater control over the environment and the self. At the same time this freedom of decision has been associated with the development of a consciousness of right and wrong, a discriminative awareness of right and wrong.

What could be the source of this causal chain? Did this causal chain come from nothing and happen as a matter of chance? It is many times more absurd to believe that this causal chain came from nothing and was due to chance than it would be to believe that you could get a map of the world by spilling a glass of water on the floor.[11]

It should be no surprise to find that the law of causality which is essential for the operation of the laws of the physical universe, the laws which govern plant and animal life, and the laws of the development of mind, leads us to the values of the Natural Moral Law, such as love, justice, mercy, rights, responsibilities, beauty—and to God. In other words, to values and high concepts which cannot be literally weighed or counted.

I submit that the hopes of the future of man rest primarily on an urge to possess those values in life which cannot be weighed or counted. Provided the basic necessities of life are available, true happiness in life comes from things which can not be weighed or counted, and from pleasures for which repentance is not required.

History and reflection have convinced me that the certainty of the primacy of spiritual and moral values rests on whether a Divine Personality, who represents Divine Perfection, exists or does not exist in the faith which guides human behavior. Our intellect reveals the unity and order in the universe, and the principle of causality. But these facts do not constitute a religion, nor a religion with permanency, unless they are permitted to operate in our everyday conduct on the basis of the freedom to make decisions and the concept of the Fatherhood of God and the consequent brotherhood of man.

If the better earth life is to be maintained, with the upward trend characteristic of the past, Divine guidance will be required. Recent sad, sickening, tragic historical events demonstrate that morality, truth, justice, mercy and freedom lead a dastardly existence when not rooted in applied theism. Under Nazi paganistic state socialism and under atheistic communism the most cherished God-given possessions of man are profaned and tramped into the mire.[12]

Only in a moral world, a world of responsibility, can man be free and live as a human being should. Men are truly equal and free only as creatures of God, because only as the children of God and only in the sight of God and ultimate moral law are men truly equal. If God and the ultimate moral law are denied, there can be no absolute argument against slavery, against "might makes right" and man's greedy exploitation of man. If human beings have no absolute intrinsic value, no absolute intrinsic freedom of decision, no absolute liberty, no absolute duties, they possess only extrinsic value and may be used as chattels, slaves or serfs by those who have the intelligence and power. Rights given to man by God can be taken away only by God, but rights given to man by man or man-made institutions can be denied or taken away by man or man-made institutions. Unless inalienable rights come from the Ultimate, from the Creator, it is irrational to say that human beings have rights which no man-made institution may ignore or deny. Man has no absolute claim of intrinsic worth and dignity, no absolute duties and responsibilities, except as a creature of God.

Is the brotherhood of man a concession of a man-made materialistic State, with expediency the only guide of individual and governmental conduct? Or is it derived from the Fatherhood of God? Which source will guarantee it the greatest permanency? Does freedom come from freedom of

[240

the spirit, from freedom of decision of the individual mind? Or is it a concession of a materialistic society? How can freedom of choice and liberty exist when a person is a creature of the State?

In the absence of a belief in the intrinsic worth and dignity of the individual, moral enormities and atrocities occur, and are justified by the doctrine of "superior orders" and the doctrine that the welfare of the State is the supreme good and end, and that the end justifies *any* means. This was the dilemma at Nuremberg. How could the Nazi leaders and doctors who were responsible for the atrocities be indicted and convicted when they were obeying Nazi law and orders?[13] They could be indicted and convicted only under the Eternal Natural Law of God, called in condescension to the atheistic Russian representatives the Laws of Humanity. If man-made law is the sole source of basic human rights, why condemn the Nazi assault on Jews, Gypsies, Poles, and political enemies? Why condemn the assault on the Hungarian Patriots? Under Nazi laws Jews had no rights. Under Red Communist laws the Hungarian Patriots had no rights. Under the communist governments behind the "iron curtain" no human being has inalienable rights. If inalienable rights exist, what made them inalienable? If man did not create the world, how can he delegate to himself the creation of his worth, dignity, rights, duties, freedom of choice, and liberty? You always get into a causal chain which leads to God unless you arbitrarily dismiss it from consideration before you arrive.

We see too much evidence in contemporary American life indicating that the American form of democracy is being undermined. It is being slowly secularized and deprived of its religious and spiritual foundation. There are too many attempts in the Western World to preserve the inviolability of human rights after surrendering or denying their ultimate Divine source. The spiritual capital and the fruits of Christianity cannot survive if their roots are destroyed, or mutilated, or left uncultivated.

By Their Works You Shall Know Them

I shall not refer to deistic humanism, pantheism, and other philosophies because I am convinced that Lenin was correct, at least insofar as contemporary history is concerned, when he concluded in effect: The future will be either

(1) The Absolute of Matter, which is Atheistic Materialism or Atheistic Communism, or

(2) The Absolute of Metaphysical Reason, which is a Theistic God whose fullest revelation was in the person of Jesus Christ.

Today, whether we like it or not, most of the material power in the world is divided into the two foregoing camps. The Theistic camp is presumed to possess, in addition, moral and spiritual power. The Atheistic camp of Marx and Lenin has the destruction of "Capitalism" and Theism as its end, denies the existence of God and unchangeable principles, has expediency as its only ethic, and considers good any type of treachery or brutality which adds to the achievement of its end. After "Capitalism" is dead and the people have forgotten all moral and religious ideas based on a belief in God, a new morality would be established. It would be a "class or State morality"; not a morality based on individual morality.

The inconsistency in the Marxian-Leninist philosophy is

that since there are no unchangeable principles, the expediency of the day would be subject to change. This means that conflict between the "governing elite class" and the "wish-to-be-a-governing-elite-class" would repeatedly occur. And because of the lack of basic moral inhibitions treachery and brutal conflict would prevail. The only other possible but less likely alternative to Marxism-Leninism is a system like that of social insects, a dictatorship, which is contrary to the basic nature of man. Man is more than matter, more than an insect, more than a mob led by a dictator.

The only place where a form of communism has ever worked satisfactorily, but not perfectly, is in a convent or monastery. But these successful communistic groups were not built by the use of concentration camps, treachery, and torture. They were built by revolutions which occur in the souls of men. They are operated on the basis of a belief in the natural moral law of God.

The battle now being waged is to the death of one or the other camp. In the first three centuries of the Christian era eleven million persons were put to death because they preferred to die for Christianity rather than to live for paganistic materialism. From 1939 to 1945 at least fifteen million people died in concentration camps because they would not live for paganistic Nazi State Socialism. In the defense of the rights of the human person and the defense of freedom we of today must be prepared to give our lives.

Since 1933 we have witnessed the effect of atheistic or paganistic materialism on the conduct of the ruling class of great groups of people. While the teaching of morals, ethics, philosophy and religion has declined in secular schools and colleges, and even in Sunday schools, in Western Civilization, the one-time considered innocent philosophy of Karl Marx and Nietzsche has been transplanted from the "ivory towers" of academic discussion to head a revolution among millions of illiterate, impoverished and oppressed people who have been too busy trying to keep body and soul together to give a thought to any other subject. The aggressive leaders of this revolution have manifested either *atheism of the intellect,* their gods being race, class, science, and progress, or *atheism of the will,* their gods being power, fame, and wealth. The abhorrent nature of their conduct is too well known to warrant mention again, and is not a recommendation for atheism or barren agnosticism of any sort or description.

Also, note the behavior of the individual atheist or pagan when he is confronted with adversity and the materialistic reason for living is crushed. Suicide is frequently their solution. When the purpose of living no longer exists, as revealed in suicide notes, self-destruction is frequently resorted to—as in the case of alcoholics.[14] When Hitler and his gang despoiled the *unorthodox* German Jews of their wealth, fame and power, many committed suicide. This was not true of the *orthodox* Jews; their reason for living was made more distinct and precious by adversity. The person who really believes in God never lacks for an inspiring, impelling and noble reason for living.

Furthermore, no human agency, having been given or having taken by force the privilege of physical and/or economic coercion, whether it be a ruling gang, a monarchy, a mob, a labor union, a professional or economic monopoly, a bureaucratic group inside or outside government, can escape a significant degree of corruption. Power grabbed by force or obtained and held by chicanery, and subject to no direct

[244

structural and functional check of the governed, is bound to become corrupt. In the case of atheists the corruption is bound to be amplified manifoldly.

The Survival Values of a Belief in God

There are three reasons why a belief in God can never be stamped out.

First, the only educational system which is designed for all men, for all exigencies, and for all time, is based on Theism as demonstrated perfectly in the Person and life of Jesus Christ. *Naturalistic education,* the goal of which is health and pleasure, is not for the chronically ill and the hopelessly crippled or diseased person. *Pragmatic education* is not for the inefficient and unadaptable person. *Humanistic education* is not for the unlearned and purely mechanically minded person. But *Theistic religious education* based on Jesus Christ is for all sorts of persons—in the colleges, in the market place, in the home, in the hospital, in the slums, in prison, or in battle. Theistic belief in God yields a power which guarantees that no absolute disaster can happen to any person having such belief. Biologically, religion may be defined as the worship of a higher power from a sense of need. It will be exceedingly difficult to suppress this need in the large majority of human beings.

Second, a belief in God is requisite to give a complete meaning to life and the universe, and thoughtful persons will *always* seek for such a meaning.

Third, children will be born for a long time to come. And, regardless of repeated attacks either by the sophisticated, confused, irrational, or by the rational sincere mind, the basic aspects of the development of the mind and thought of the child will continue to exist as long as the machinery for the development of mind interacts with sense experience as it has in the past, and as long as the universe continues to operate as it has in the past. It would appear that the adult mind will continue to react to the principles of natural law and rational thought, unless it were blocked or deviated by some irrational cause from its natural course of development. The mind of practically all the great benefactors of man did not depart from the basic principles of the basic laws which govern Nature and its highest function, thought. They made a search beyond the immediate facts of the sense perceptions to find the cause and to discover new truth, and arrived at a belief in God.

It is for these reasons that we may be of good cheer. Survival and evolutionary value are attached only to those things which are adaptable to and are good for all people under all conditions for all the time. That is why the trend of religious faith and thought, and its effect on the individual and society, has been constantly upward throughout the ages regardless of the rise and fall of civilizations. More important, the basic principles of unsophisticated and rational thought and belief will always rise again with the birth of every child. Let us recall that a little child manifests reason, faith, hope and love. Is this why Jesus Christ stressed the *child* aspect? For example:

"Suffer the little children to come unto Me; forbid them not; for to such belongeth the Kingdom of God." (Mark 10: 14)

"Whosoever shall not receive the Kingdom of God as a little child, he shall in no wise enter therein." (Luke 18: 11)

[246

"Except ye turn, and become as little children, ye shall in no wise enter into the Kingdom of Heaven." (Matthew 18: 3)

"Except one be born anew, he cannot see the Kingdom of God." (John 3: 3)

As Max Planck, the scientist who opened the way to the inside of the atom, has said: "'Religion and Natural Science are fighting a joint battle in an incessant, never-relaxing crusade against skepticism, against dogmatism, and against superstition; and the rallying cry in this crusade has always been, and always will be: On to God!'"

I shall close with a quotation from Louis Pasteur who ranks near the top of the list of the greatest benefactors of mankind:

"If someone tells me that in making these conclusions I have gone beyond the facts, I reply: 'It is true that I have freely put myself among ideas which cannot always be rigorously proved. That is my way of looking at things.'"

If I have gone beyond the facts, and have made errors, please point them out to me. I am always anxious to learn.

DR. IVY'S NOTES

¹ Unfortunately those who deny or doubt the existence of God and question the validity of formal logical proof receive more publicity than those who do not deny or doubt.

² I am a Christian theist.

³ Reason precedes faith. Reason operates to prove those things which are provable. Faith is based on reason but goes beyond (transcends) reason to establish a base on which to believe things which are either sure, or very probable, or possible, but have not yet been established by their actual occurrence or by their becoming visible, though their occurrence and existence can be established by formal logic on the basis of experience. That is, *faith goes beyond but does not contradict the truth which reason can prove.* Hope is based on reason and faith, and when so based it should energize the search for those good things which should be. Love also should be based on reason and faith, because the natural conduct of all living things is based on the natural law of preservation of self and the species. And because God is the ultimate Source of our individual worth, dignity, rights and duties, without which we are "things" and may be used as chattels (as is done under atheistic materialism or paganism, where individuals are creatures of the State), we should love God above all and obey His natural laws. If we really love God, we shall knowingly do nothing which will injure ourselves or a fellow member of the species.

⁴ Thomas Jefferson, however, may have believed that the existence of God and of inalienable rights was something intuitive and that there should be no doubt about it. His position may have been as follows: The very idea of a Supreme Being implies His existence. The more universally applicable an idea, the greater is its reality, and the greater its causal efficiency. The intuitive Supreme Universal is the Supreme Cause, the Supreme Good, Truth, Beauty, Love and Reality. Divine guidance must be postulated if we are to maintain these particularities and others associated with them.

[248

⁵Causality, I maintain, is not anthropomorphic (the addition of human characteristics to things not human) because the existence of causality, like any other existence, arises *not* from sense experience alone but from an interaction of sense experience with the machinery of mind. It is not a product which is entirely sense experience or entirely mind, or a product *per se* of the machinery for the production of mind. Sense experience and mind are all we have with which to know our environment and give it meaning.

Kant maintained that the principle of causality is not an objective value and that the judgment of the operation of causality in everyday life is used only to regulate the unification of sense experience. He believed, however, that causality is a necessary and universal principle. The view of Kant, that causality is not an objective value, is incorrect because it holds that a judgment which is not entirely derived from sense experience must be due entirely to an inherent structure of the mind. But this is only partly true. A judgment is the *result* of the interaction of sense experience with the machinery of the mind, and the previously developed mind. Even the machinery of a simple nervous reflex is so designed as to yield a purposeful response to a stimulus (material cause).

Hume claimed that it is incorrect to believe anything which our senses do not reveal. He argued that our senses observe only changes or a succession of events, antecedents and consequences, *not* causes and effects, and since we cannot see causality we cannot know it. He concludes that there is nothing in thought which requires us to believe that because something happens it must be caused. This view is incorrect because it recognizes only a part of sense experience. The succession of events is only a part of the total picture because the quality and quantity of the change are ignored; quality and quantity place the change in direct relation with a qualitative and quantitative cause, and the intellect either sees the reason for the change or starts a search for it.

ᶠ I heard Will Durant, the "outliner of philosophy," make a statement to the effect that the only reason why many philosophers became famous was that they had written obscurely or had made very profound errors. I believe there is considerable truth in this view, although I enjoy and gain from reading their writings. Some of these writers should restudy Aristotle, the Bible, and the Scholastics. Because, in science, *sequence* is usually the best way to avoid error and to stick to the trend and basic principles for the discovery of truth. At least, if learning is not started in an historical sequence the scholar soon should revert to it and check his conclusions against the historical sequence.

ᵀMetaphysics deals with an analysis of experience and the principles of thought.

249]

⁸ I maintain that the cosmological and teleological proofs are valid, if the category of cause is admitted as established. The observed facts force me to insist that it is established and that any other position is irrational.

⁹ The Scholastics acknowledged that certain items of creed could not be established by logic, but had to be accepted by faith. One was the doctrine of the Divine Trinity.

¹⁰ "But of the tree of the knowledge of good and evil thou shalt not eat; for in the day that thou eatest thereof thou shalt surely die." (Genesis 2:17)

¹¹ If chance were a factor, it appears that someone must have loaded the dice.

¹² If today a man marries the ruling group of an irrational "ism," such as atheistic or paganistic materialism, recent history shows that he has married a widow or a concentration camp.

¹³ I specify Nazi law because the codified German Law and Jurisprudence were contrary to much of Nazi law, which was based on edicts of Hitler and his gang.

¹⁴ Most alcoholics when they "hit the bottom" have no feeling of individual worth or dignity, and have lost any purpose for living that they may have had. When a careful study was made, it was found that 50 percent of suicides were alcoholics. Some psychiatrists refer to drunkenness as the commission of temporary suicide. Other suicides were drunk on power, fame, and wealth. All lacked belief in God.